Praise for *The Dep* Mysticism, Phy

"Mary Conrow Coelho has written a remarkable new book, The Depth of Our Belonging: Mysticism, Physics and Healing. *As Mary came to understand the meaning of the evolutionary story and of the depths of numinous matter, she realized to her great joy that mystical experiences are not strange or unusual. Rather, they are integral to the natural world and to our very being. This transformed world view enabled her to find healing from the consequences of a family tragedy when she was just an infant and a young child. In her courageous book, we are invited to move from self-doubt and alienation to deep belonging in a universe that unfolds with endless creativity. Highly recommended."* —Brian Thomas Swimme, Professor of Cosmology, California Institute of Integral Studies

"In this enlightening and beautifully illustrated book, Mary Coelho joins discoveries in new physics with mystical wisdom to reset our orientation to the inner and outer life. In her hopeful vision, the transformation of the self and the beneficence of the natural world spring from the underlying sacred Presence or seamless plenum, opening a path of healing for our wounded souls and for our world." —Beverly Lanzetta, Ph.D., contemplative scholar and author of *A New Silence: Spiritual Practices and Formation for the Monk Within.*

"A soulful and down-to-earth treatment of an ever-burgeoning topic—the intersection of science and mysticism. What gives Mary's heartfelt account a spirit is the personal healing story that weaves through the book. What makes it so accessible is her lucid and well researched exposition of the un-visualizable quantum field that we now believe underpins all of existence and may turn out to be the sacred presence that mystics all over the world have tapped into over many millennia. I would be remiss in my praise for the book if I didn't mention her stunning and breathtaking art that brings it all to life."* —Sarbmeet Kanwal, Professor of Physics at Brookdale Community College, Lincroft, New Jersey.

Other Books by Mary Conrow Coelho

Mary Conrow Coelho, 2015. *Recovering Sacred Presence in a Disenchanted World*. Wallingford, PA: Pendle Hill Pamphlet #433.

Mary Conrow Coelho, 2002. *Awakening Universe Emerging Personhood*: The Power of Contemplation In An Evolving Universe. Levering, MI: Wyndham Hall Press.

Jerome M. Neufelder and Mary C. Coelho, 1982. *Writings on Spiritual Direction by Great Christian Masters*. New York NY: Seabury Press.

Front Cover Painting: Tree of Life

The discovery by physicists of the unseen generative ground (the light shining inside the geometric, rectangular pattern) is added within the traditional image of the tree of life. The painting celebrates the unity of life and the numinous, energetic interiority permeating our world and our person now recognized by both physicists and experienced by people of many spiritual traditions. The full painting is on page 51. All the paintings in this book are by the author.

The Depth of Our Belonging Mysticism, Physics, and Healing

Mary Conrow Coelho

Dedication:

To my mother, Frances Gardiner Conrow, who cared for her infant daughter in the midst of one of the most profound griefs that anyone is called to endure, the loss of a young child. May this book be worthy of her strength.

Producciones de la Hamaca

Published by *Producciones de la Hamaca,* Caye Caulker, Belize

Paperback ISBN: 978-976-8273-17-8

E-book ISBN 978-976-8273-18-5

Producciones de la Hamaca is dedicated to:

—Celebration and documentation of Earth
    and all her inhabitants,
—Restoration and conservation of Earth's
    natural resources,
—Creative expression of the sacredness of
    Earth and Spirit.

Contents

Preface

In the past two centuries there have been major, unanticipated discoveries about which many of us have little knowledge, yet they are of great personal and cultural importance. These pages explore two of these discoveries that illumine the contemplative life and mystical experience, offering a pathway within which to seek healing and wisdom. They bring us insights that help free us from an outdated worldview that has caused suffering too often and distanced us from the heart of our identity.

One discovery is that physicists are now telling us that there is a nonvisible, non-material generative power throughout the world that is the foundational reality of the universe. It is interior to our very being as well as to the trees, the rocks and everything around us. Although the initial breakthrough that would lead to this discovery occurred in the 19th century, it was in the 1940s that the quantum field was experimentally verified. The atoms that form within it are energy patterns bringing a radical change in our understanding of the very matter of our bodies and all the manifest world. Brian Swimme suggests the name "all-nourishing abyss" for this interiority that is hidden to daily consciousness. In this book the phrase "seamless plenum" will be used. The phrase is based on the description of the invisible interior realm as interconnected, and, therefore, "seamless", and also a highly energetic ocean of potentiality, a "plenum."

The second great breakthrough that is part of the assumptions behind the exploration in these pages is our new origin story, now extended far beyond the evolution of species here on Earth to include the great flaring forth 13.8 billion years ago. It is a magnificent story that invites us to pause for careful reflection about our identity given our remarkable origins. After the creation of the hydrogen atom early in the history of the universe, heavier atoms were created in large stars, an astounding, dramatic process that is part of our new origin story. Over the millennia here on earth, the matter of our daily world was created by the complex interactions of these atoms made in stars. The early universe is thought to have had a latent form of consciousness so the complexification of matter over the millennia also involves the evolution of consciousness.

There are several profoundly hopeful dimensions of these epic discoveries. While the change in our understanding of matter is new in the western world of science, there is a surprising congruence with many, sometimes centuries old, mystical traditions and spiritual insights. We are invited to an exciting, urgent inquiry as the alienation of human consciousness from Earth and from each other needs to change and to be healed. Because of the remarkable changes in understanding our identity as now offered by the breakthrough discoveries in science, many of the insights and teachings of our spiritual traditions find a home. The spiritual journey and the heartening fulfillment that spiritual traditions have promised can now move to a central place in our culture. We can abandon some outdated theologies while at the same time embracing many traditional spiritual insights and practices and explore new possibilities. This is the primary focus of this book.

These pages are an invitation for the reader to personally explore the significance of these discoveries. Having been a graduate student in science, I know firsthand how our mechanistic science that claims full explanatory power over our lives can devalue and even discredit mystical experiences and the sacred presence that people have come to know experientially for centuries. The dualism of the western world has divided mind and soul, body and spirit, so there has not been a ready understanding of a pathway to healing, nor a home for the spiritual journey and mystical experience. Charles Tart has written of "the useless and unnecessary suffering caused by personally internalized scientific models of humanity that completely reject the spiritual, that see us as nothing but meat computers in a meaningless material universe."[1]

With these two major recent discoveries by scientists we find ourselves within a fundamentally changed worldview, placing us in a different relationship to spirituality. Recognizing this new situation, I have sought to find a home for mystical experience and also healing from psychological and spiritual wounding which was caused in my family by the loss of a child in my family of origin. The insights described in these pages arise from a search for a deep, healing belonging. Although focusing on a particular, unique personal story, the fundamental patterns of the pathway described will be recognized as of value to others searching for healing and a profound belonging.

In Chapter One "Awakening Within Tragedy" I tell the story of the loss to my parents and the cost to me when my four-year-old brother died when I was an infant. I also describe in this chapter an awakening, mystical experience that changed the direction of my life. These two events have been central to my personal need to find a resolution of the western split separating spirit from the natural world so I might be confidant there is an inner psychological and spiritual foundation for a healing journey. A brief telling of the evolutionary story ends the chapter as it brings a profound belonging when understood together with our new understanding of matter described in the second chapter.

Chapter Two "A Transformed Understanding of Matter" seeks to outline in an accessible manner the discoveries about matter offered by quantum physics. We must not be intimidated by the reputation of physics as being inaccessible and difficult. We describe most remarkable discoveries about matter that move us out of the sometimes destructive, mechanistic worldview of recent centuries which claimed full explanatory power about the nature of our world. Matter is not what we have commonly thought, although this is not to deny the experiences of our senses and daily awareness and the value of many of the discoveries of recent centuries.

Chapter Three, "Listening to Mystic's Words in the Context of the Radical Discoveries by Physicists," proposes that the new physics and the mystical tradition and the contemplative pathway now share some important commonalities of insight. Reflections on the significance of this for the individual and the culture are offered.

In Chapter Four "Becoming Fully Conscious Participants in the Unfolding Story", some thoughts about entering into and participating in the integration proposed in Chapter III are explored. For many people it involves embrace of suffering and seeking a pathway to healing. We may become a different person, perhaps being wise on occasion and finding creative expression of our remarkable identity that is coming to consciousness now after 13.8 billion years of our still unfolding epic creation story.

Mary Conrow Coelho, MDiv, PhD, Historical Theology

Acknowledgements

I am very grateful to those who have accompanied me on the search to understand the spiritual significance of the major changes in our understanding of human identity offered by the evolutionary story and the remarkable discoveries about the nature of the very matter of our bodies and the natural world. After I was initially introduced to the changes in Brian Swimme's film series *Canticle to the Cosmos* in the early 1990s, I wanted to explore and celebrate the new understandings. I traveled by train from New York City to Princeton, New Jersey, to meet with the Epic of Evolution Group. Jennifer Morgan kindly picked me up at the train station. Many in the group, including Jack Heckelman, the founder, had studied with Sr. Miriam MacGillis at Genesis Farm in northern New Jersey. We talked and rejoiced in our awakening realizations. In New York City several of us formed a group around ecological concerns and the study of some aspects of the New Story. That group continues to this day. I am indebted particularly to Janet Soderberg and Tom Goodridge, companions for many years in that group. I am grateful to John Grimm and Mary Evelyn Tucker who organized the annual meetings of the board of the American Teilhard Association, a luncheon and a lecture, which brought a day of companionship and learning over many years.

When I moved to Cambridge, Massachusetts, in the early 2000s, we formed a New Story Group at the Friends Meeting at Cambridge, which has brought companionship and serious inquiry now for fifteen years. David Damm-Luhr, Art Klipfel , Nan Lee, Gwen Noyes and I, with Severyn Bruyn as a consultant, formed the original group. We have all learned together as we watched film series, read several books, organized seminars and discussed countless topics. We have published two pamphlets, the first of which Philip Clayton helped us write and a second was entitled "Quakers and the New Story: Healing Ourselves and the Earth." Gwen Noyes and Art Klipfel invited us to their weekend home on Cape Cod where we could focus on carefully selected topics. Cornelia Parkes is now leading the group as our ongoing search for understanding continues. I thank you all for contributing greatly to my understanding and appreciation of this line of investigation.

A number of people have read and commented on parts or the entirety of this book. I am indebted to them for their responses and interest. Mary Alice Bird, Marion Foster, Nancy Wright, Judith Morse, Cornelia Parkes, Stephanie Choo, Margaret Conrow and Barbara Gardiner have all read parts or all of the book. Sam Mackintosh offered immensely helpful insights over many years of emails. Steve Martin and Sarbmeet Kanwal helped me with the chapter about quantum physics as part of the preparation for the online class "Cosmology, Consciousness and Birthing the Ecozoic" offered on Jennifer Morgan's Deeptime Network. In that online course it was a pleasure to be in touch with the community of people from around the world involved with the new story, some working within churches and others working independently.

The paintings in this book have been shown in exhibits at Mercy by the Sea in Madison, CT, at Pendle Hill in Wallingford PA, the Clare Gallery at the Church of St Anthony and St Patrick in Hartford, CT and at the Friends Meeting at Cambridge. I was also fortunate to show some of them at an online annual meeting of the American Teilhard Association and in a class offered by the Deeptime Network. I am grateful for this support of my art.

I would not have been able to write this book without the computer help from my daughter Sarah. Fortunately for me she has been working at home, so she has been upstairs available to rescue me many times.

Thank you Judy Lumb, the editor of this book, for your support, patience and careful, caring help over many months.

Thank you everyone!

Mary Conrow Coelho

25 January 2021

The Beauty of the Ancient Earth

CHAPTER ONE
Awakening Within Tragedy

One afternoon as I walked into our bedroom in New York City, without thought or intention, I was brought to my knees. I was knelt. I had not been taught as a child to kneel. I do not know how long I remained kneeling by the bed. A strong energy, previously unknown to me, pervaded my whole being. I was profoundly moved both physically and spiritually. It would eventually change the direction of my life.

I had no words to describe the experience. I had no name for it and no ability to talk about it and no understanding of what happened. Although it was of great importance to me, as it was profoundly attractive, I said nothing about it for many years. I told no one as I feared its importance to me would not be heard or I would be found foolish or troubled. I couldn't speak as I had no adequate words and, furthermore, I feared that if I spoke, the experience might be discredited. The search in these chapters is for a worldview that offers an understanding of such experiences and to encourage wide embrace by individuals and the culture of the profoundly attractive, healing numinous reality that I experienced that afternoon when I was 29 years old.

One reason, and there are several reasons, I was unable to speak about the experience is that I had been a biology student in college. One chilly evening in college as I was walking slowly across the campus, I realized that I must accept that there was no possibility of indwelling sacred Presence or "Light within" my being and within Earth, given the assumptions that I was being taught in my biology classes. In a class on evolutionary biology, the changes in living beings over time were attributed entirely to random changes in the DNA and the survivability of the fittest new organisms that developed from those random

1

events. Everything was accounted for by mechanized forces and biochemical events. There was no larger order, no patterns, no intrinsic creativity, no unity.

I realized that I would need to create personal meaning as an individual or adopt on faith the teachings of a religious community like those taught in our chapel services or my family's tradition. I had not yet had occasion to read about the "intractable division," to use Richard Tarnas's words, between mind and soul in our western tradition.[2] I was experiencing that very division firsthand as a biology student. Tragically I was being taught in a church-affiliated college that there was no ground of being, no larger order. There were required biblical classes, but I was not able to hear in those classes how the "intractable division" could be addressed in the light of the convincing explanations of 20th century science. I had no idea that the science I was learning was already outdated.

My recognition of the intractable division that chilly evening persuaded me that I must disregard and devalue the special, mysterious experiences that had occurred occasionally while playing as a child with neighbors under a beautiful, great white oak tree by the pasture. The phrase "subtle Presence" describes those experiences well. There was no home for those experiences within the reductive assumptions I was being taught in college as that world of science promised a full explanation of life. Those experiences under the tree must not have been of significance and had to be discounted.

Some years after college when I was packing to move, I even gave away my books on Quakerism, books given to me by the community I grew up in. The books carried great promise and hope, but I had to be honest that I no longer had confidence in their promise.

In addition to the profoundly attractive quality of my experience of being kneeled, it was healing. I was a different person for several weeks, becoming more confident and outgoing, able to express myself and my ideas with some strength and clarity. This temporary change brought to my awareness some personal issues, including the lack of confidence, about which I had not been conscious. I longed to know again that which I had known that afternoon. But I could only wonder if God, the God that I then assumed was outside me, the God that I had rejected, had visited me and I could hope "He" might visit once again.

In the months following that experience I thought "I know the answer to humanity's problems." This was not an arrogant claim of special intellectual understanding, as I had none, and I could not explain what was the answer. Those words were simply a phrase formed spontaneously in my mind as a way of affirming the fundamentally meaningful, life-giving experience; it certainly was not to be neglected as it was in some sense an "answer." I only knew that I wanted it to happen again, even kneeling at times hoping that physical position would be an occasion to enter again into the experience.

As I continued my graduate studies in biology, my very being, my buried personhood, my unconscious need would not let me neglect the awakening experience as it was so profoundly attractive. Although I had no understanding at the time, I had experienced something deep within me, integral to my being. In addition, unknown to me, the need for awakening and healing was indeed great so the experience could not be neglected. Eventually, I did take an evening class in downtown New York City where I learned about mysticism and begin to read the recommended books. There were occasions when it would have been appropriate and wise to ask for help in addition to the study, but I could not as I did not know how to speak about the experience. It did not belong in the culture in which I had learned to understand myself. Once I did try to tell a priest about the experience and to ask questions, but he did not understand and became impatient.

It was the reductive science I had studied that led me to abandon my spiritual hopes that chilly night while in college. The problem I eventually came to understand, is that, although the scientific method has great value, it disregards the consciousness of the person as subject, falsely separating and disregarding the knowing person from the subject of study and the unfolding cosmos. Following the awakening experience, I as the subject had to value the felt knowing of a reality of such great attractive power. The experience while on my knees and the longing it provoked, meant I must eventually change the direction of my life abandoning biology, at least temporarily.

That awakening experience showed me clearly that my biology professor's claim of the full explanatory power of the science she was teaching was deeply inadequate. I learned in the class on mysticism and through many books, that the experience on my knees in the bedroom was a "mystical experience." Mystical experiences are widely recognized and not uncommon. They are known in a great range of intensity, on widely varying occasions and in many cultures. There are countless accounts of numinous experiences during illness, while dancing, singing, listening to music, lovemaking, meditating, in nature, and as children play.

A great number of books and articles have been written about mysticism, many of which have been immensely helpful to me. People East and West have described experiences in which the restrictions of daily consciousness are overcome so individuals come to know what is perhaps more wisely called a "higher consciousness." Perhaps there are better names. It was encouraging to learn that this mode of consciousness can become more available to a person through spiritual practice, although it also occurs spontaneously. We know that following a sometimes-arduous inward journey, countless people have come to an amazing condition in which they have an ongoing awareness of the depth of the human being, the natural world, and even inanimate things. Louis Dupré, former professor of Philosophy of Religion at Yale University, writes in *Transcendent Selfhood* that this change in consciousness brings to full awareness that the soul itself rests on a divine basis.[3] Although heartened by what I was learning about mysticism, I remained unaware that I still had many assumptions from my internalized, out-of-date science, that prevented full appreciation of the significance of the mystical tradition.

When I was so powerfully influenced by the intractable division while in college, I had been mistaken to discount those special mysterious experiences, the subtle Presence I experienced under the oak tree while playing with neighbors. In the first decade of the 20th century even physics itself had moved away from its confidence in its full explanatory power as it entered the quantum world. Later I came to understand that those experiences spoke fundamentally to who I am and who people are within the emerging understanding of our identity in physics and in the many traditions of mysticism in many cultures.

A New Direction of Study

Given the power of the experience in the bedroom and the longing it evoked, I eventually found the courage to apply to

Union Theological Seminary in New York City and stop teaching biology. It was a major turn to engage and ponder the experience. I thought I was unprepared to attend a seminary because of my science background and as a Quaker I had not learned the usual language of the Protestant faiths and its creeds. Although I thought it was wrong to discontinue studying and teaching biology, I did need to change course.

Fortunately, it was at Union that I was introduced to Jungian thought and I began to work with a Jungian analyst. That became a fundamentally important adventure for me as the personal consequences of a tragedy in my family, described in the following pages, began to surface. And Jung's thought helped me to begin to question the "intractable division" I had been carefully taught in college.

Attracted by courses in mysticism and the work and thought of Ewert Cousins who promised wise, contemporary teaching, I continued to study as a graduate student at Fordham University a couple of years after finishing a Master of Divinity at Union and working in the Spiritual Direction program at General Theological Seminary. It was at Fordham University that I wrote my thesis on Teresa of Avila, the great 16th century Carmelite mystic. I wrote an article about her image of the interior castle.[4] The article describes how she changed the image of the interior castle, which is made of gold and precious stones in her earlier writing,[5] to a castle made of clear crystal or diamond in her book, *The Interior Castle*. It is within this invisible castle that all the ongoing, ever deepening mystical experiences occurred. A person may live in different "dwelling places" in the castle that are modes of being, different stages of the spiritual journey as one move closer to the center, to a transformed identity. Little did I understand at the time the full truthfulness of that image that becomes more compelling in the context of the breakthroughs in contemporary physics that have changed our understanding of matter, the subject of the next chapter.

Perhaps my work and study of her image of the interiority of her being as a castle made of clear crystal helped to prepare me to hear the breakthroughs in physics a few years later. Although they came from radically different disciplines of human inquiry, they have fundamentally important insight in common which I will contend is revelatory of human identity. Although the deterministic world of my college years had not yet been broken open by the changes in science itself, the fruits of my studies at Fordham are part of these reflections. I received a PhD in Historical Theology from Fordham University.

A Tragedy in My Family of Origin

It was not only the objectivized science I was taught in college that explains the long delay in my embrace of the fundamental spiritual identity of my person. There was another reason. Why was I willing to abandon the early experiences under the oak tree, subtle though they were, and eventually leave the religious tradition of my youth for several years? Why was I vulnerable to those claims of a worldview denying the intrinsic spiritual dimension of the human person? The central reason for the need to recover the lost dimension of my being and thereby find healing was the costly personal consequences resulting from the death of my four-year-old brother when I was an infant.

As a child I sometimes fleetingly looked at the photograph of a little boy on my mother's bedroom bureau, but I did not ask about him and my mother did not explain who he was. To this day I remember where the framed color photograph stood on the bureau. Some years later I learned that the little boy, David, my brother, died of spinal meningitis when he was almost four years old.

On a cold March day when David was playing outside, he got cold and wet when he fell into a ditch on the farm. When he developed a fever, it was first thought he had an ear infection. While his mother, who was nine months pregnant, cared for David, contractions began so she was taken to the hospital where I was born.

Still at home, David's condition worsened. He was taken to the same hospital where his mother and newborn sister were. For fear the disease would spread to my mother and her infant daughter she could not visit David who was cared for on another floor of the hospital. David died four days later as there was no treatment for spinal meningitis at that time. David was buried before my mother and I came home from the hospital.

I cannot imagine my mother's dread of returning to our home as there would be a terrible emptiness without David. It would be too quiet as Ken, David's five-year-old brother, had no one to play with. Toys would stay on the shelf. When Ken was told his brother had gone to heaven, Ken asked why David had not taken his shoes. Raw effort was required on my mother's part to provide the bare minimum of essential care for me and her family. She could not nurse her daughter. My father became silent. On occasion he was given to angry outbursts, perhaps an expression of his loss. It is not surprising that for many years, come March, my birthday would not be celebrated.

I was not given the gift of being deeply loved and embraced by my mother during those early months and years. How can a mother fully care for and express her love for her infant in the midst of one of the most difficult human experiences, the loss of a young child? Maternal love and care nurtures and draws forth the awakening of the personhood of the infant. I was among the many people who have not been given this gift of love and nurture of their full being.

This early loss is part of the reason why I was not able to speak about the mystical experience for years. I had learned to repress and hide from the feelings that were a consequence of the tragic loss of a full nurturing relationship with my mother; the loss could not be spoken about as it was costly and touched too deeply. Consequently, I also hid the strong feelings that the awakening experience evoked. I did not know how to engage with mystical experiences as I did not know how to engage the tragic deprivation. They lived too closely together. Spiritual teachers promise a spiritual depth that is present regardless of the wounding, but the Presence is often hidden in the dark night.

A powerful longing to belong deeply was awakened by the experience on my knees. It was a longing to recover the love and belonging that was partially lost in my infancy and childhood that the awakening experience promised is possible. It is a longing that is widespread as many families cannot provide a home with nurturing love. The personal cost of the loss of maternal love experienced by the children in the ongoing tragedy of the separation of parents and children at the border between the United States and Mexico is too great for words.

The destruction of forests and meadows, places that are often the occasion of spiritual awakening as children play, means a significant loss for many people of important occasions of awakening. Many young people are growing up without occasion for the full awakening of identity. There is no ready assumption of being part of the human family, Earth and its many beings. They, as was I, are not deeply at home. The tragic "intractable division" that Richard Tarnas identified can enable prolonged hiding of personal loss as one can live and hide in the objectified world for many years.

For many years, I did not know how to ask for help or even realize I needed it. I did not ask enough questions at the seminary, although there was a gradual eroding of my narrow, objectified assumptions. Asking for help meant I did not know; to ask for help would be an admission I could not be independent as I had been forced to be given my mother's paralyzing suffering.

And perhaps a request for help would fail, repeating the experience of my needs not being fully met by my mother as a consequence of the costly tragedy. I could read and study and try to figure things out myself. In both high school and college, I had avoided my loneliness by being busy and achieving in sports and academics. Yet for many years I still hoped the promised "Light within" would make itself known to me. While in college, even after that chilly dark night when I realized the consequences of the objectified worldview I was studying, I still attended a small Quaker meeting organized by a college professor.

A multiple-choice test I once took in a workshop told me that I had a high need to achieve. It took me many years to appreciate the full significance of that information. I now understand that it is not surprising given the loss of full maternal love very early in my life. I had to find a way to earn a response and attention from others when I was not confident it would be given naturally and spontaneously. My need to achieve was a defense similar to these words I once read: "Feeling the need to be busy all the time is a trauma response and fear-based distraction from what you would be forced to acknowledge and feel if you slowed down." Achievement does offer some identity when there has been a weakening of the more fundamental identity of the awakening Self in relation to the mother, father, and family. It is not surprising that I have found it difficult to sit quietly to meditate as I have felt impelled to be busy, to accomplish something. It would take many years to begin to be aware of and experience the inner suffering that I long avoided.

Ripening Bounty

Life on a Farm

Growing up on a working farm saved my life from a deeper wounding. Although it was not my initial intention, the emerging worldview I have come to understand and describe in these pages has become, among other things, a testimony to the great importance of the natural world for the spiritual and emotional life of the individual, not to mention our complete dependence on it for water, fresh air, and food. I think I would not have thrived to the degree that I have without being at home on a farm with space to ride my bicycle, to build huts with bundled cornstalks, to make miniature villages with sticks and acorns in the sand, to sled down the barn hill, to ice skate on the pond, to roll large balls of snow to make snowmen and forts, to pick blackberries, to watch as baskets of ripe, bright red tomatoes were stacked high on the truck, to climb the hemlocks, to hear the great horned owls that spent the night in the hemlocks, and to play with neighborhood boys.

During grade school I played during the long summer hours with Bruce and Doug Pine, two boys a couple of years younger than I, who lived down the lane and across the street. I particularly remember the bicycle shows we put on; we actually stood on the seats of the bicycle while leaning over to hold the handlebars but also sometimes standing straight up! The farm, all the animals, and the hemlocks and sycamore trees all offered a home of unquestioned belonging. I was indigenous, as were my parents and grandparents, to the land I was born on. It nourished me in many ways beyond words. Several years ago I hung a picture of the face of a barn owl among the display of family photographs because the barn owl was a marvelous part of our daily life as we watched it fly with such majesty in and out of the barn every night.

Barn Owl

Butterfly

Teilhard de Chardin wrote about the passivities of our lives, a term which means quite simply that which is not done by us but is by definition undergone. As he describes the two dimensions of our lives—the active and the passive, he explains that "from our point of view, the active occupies first place because we prefer it and because it is more easily perceived. But in the reality of things the passive is immeasurably the wider and the deeper part."[6] He describes many passivities, including those of aging and dying. David's tragic death was a major passivity for my mother and father, for me and for Ken, and also for my children and friends because it had a profound, costly effect on my life that affected my capacity for relationship. The loss of love <u>and the ability to love is a tragedy</u> easily carried <u>forward to the next generation</u>, becoming a passivity for the next generation. There is now available to us all, a change in worldview that offers a home in which the great passivities of life can be addressed with greater fruitfulness.

New York City

I lived with my husband Jaime for more than 35 years in New York City. We had three children, Daniel, Chris, and Sarah. There is a wealth of resources available in the city to which I am deeply indebted. A few paintings speak to the beauty and diversity of the city.

West 125th Street

Shadow of Light

Edgecombe Avenue

Metropolitan Opera

View from the Elevated

Late Afternoon Light

Gate to the Garden

This was painted in Argentina, my husband's home country where we lived for four years. Jaime's ancestors once lived on an estancia in the heart of the pampas where they had turned a natural grassland into an elegant park with trees and flowering plants that surround the house and out-buildings!

A Transformed Worldview

One evening in the early 1990s my life suddenly changed again. I was with a small group gathered to watch a video in a church on Central Park West in New York City. The speaker in the video said: "A full teaching of physics and geology requires teaching the interior, nonvisible depth that pervades all of matter."[7] My heart stirred with these words. The idea that teaching physics, no less, requires teaching interior depth certainly caught my attention. What interior depth could the physicist and mathematical cosmologist, Brian Swimme, be talking about? In the classrooms of biology, chemistry and introductory physics that I had studied, there was no mention of interior depth, only descriptions of the positions of the electrons and the nucleus of the atom which I thought of, without much reflection, as very small particles that structure the atom. While not fully understanding what Swimme was saying, I recognized he was speaking about a world radically different from the classical physics of my student days.

I learned later that Brian Swimme also teaches, as do other physicists, that the "interior, nonvisible depth" is 99.99% of the atom; as impossible to comprehend as this initially seems.[8] Although the percentage is disputed, Swimme writes "The volume of elementary particles is extremely small when compared to the volume of the atoms that they form. Thus, the essential nature of any atom is less material then it is 'empty space.' From this perspective we can begin to see that the root foundation of anything and any being is not the matter out of which it is composed so much as the matter together with the power that gives rise to matter."[9] It is important to ponder our assumptions about the nature of matter as our common ideas need to change radically.

Sometimes people have taught that the atom is empty. This means empty of that which can be measured and known by the senses and their extensions with scientific instruments. But it is not the best description since although empty in this sense, it is not empty given the pattern of nonvisible energy. Watching the video, I knew I needed to know what Swimme was talking about as I am made of atoms which comprise my very being so this non-material realm pervades my being. Such an unexpected discovery made by physicists certainly attracts attention. And furthermore, when all the gases and all particles have been removed from around us, so the space around us is really empty space from the perspective of our senses and our instruments, the nonmaterial, nonvisible realm is present. I was profoundly moved because I knew this breakthrough in science was opening a door from science into the world of spirituality.

Recovering Our Integral Belonging

Listening several evenings to the series of videos in the church on Central Park West, I also learned that the evolutionary story had changed nearly beyond recognition since I had studied it in college and taught it to high school students. For the first time the entire human/Earth community has in this story a single creation or origin myth.[10] As the Copernican revolution was one of the events that brought the great split between science and religion in the west, I began to dare to hope that the changes now available from science will be part of healing that intractable split that had been so difficult for me and so many others. This is not to deny the great value of the fruitful and life-saving discoveries of science but the discoveries that invite us to embrace our new origin story and our transformed understanding of matter, are of profound importance. Thomas Berry writes that "we will recover our sense of wonder and our sense of the sacred only if we appreciate the universe beyond ourselves as a revelatory experience of the numinous presence when all things come into being."[11]

In light of the discovery of "the interior, nonvisible depth that pervades all of matter," I realized I might find an understanding of that transformative experience on my knees. The exploration in these pages on finding a fundamental home for mysticism is based on our transformed understanding of matter, in the context of the evolutionary universe.

Key Insights from our New Origin Story

The cosmic evolutionary story, along with the change in our understanding of matter are central to what some people are calling the "New Story" or the "Great Story" that fundamentally changes many commonly held Western assumptions about Earth and our self-understanding as conscious, self-aware earth beings. In 1978 Thomas Berry first published his path-breaking essay "The New Story" where "he called for a coming together of science and the humanities to narrate the great epic of evolution."[12] The awakening in our contemporary culture to the comprehensive evolutionary story based on the work of thousands of people is a great intellectual achievement of the modern age. It is a nearly unbelievable epic narrative to be deeply pondered. I have discovered to my joy that the epic of evolution, together with the unexpected changes in our understanding of the nature of matter, opens the door to soul-nourishing and soul-satisfying deep, full belonging within daily life. It could not be more important.

One of the remarkable discoveries that I learned during those evenings watching those videos in the church on Central Park West is that most of the atoms in our bodies were made in stars. Where have I been? I had never heard that before. Furthermore, is the universe really 13.8 billion years old? I was excited and amazed. I went to the American Museum of Natural History in New York City in search of slides of the life cycle of stars, pictures of galaxies and exploding supernova to illustrate

Born with a Bang

our new origin story in a slide show that I decided to prepare. I also found slides depicting the formation of Earth an estimated 4.6 billion years ago as well as slides of the more familiar story of the creatures who left a fossil record. I pondered how this long history, a story with great creativity and also destructive periods, informs human identity, our daily lives and the human place on Earth and in the cosmos.

A Single Energy Event

Brian Swimme writes this summary statement: "we are enveloped by a universe that is a single energetic event, a whole, a unified, multiform, and glorious outpouring of being."[13] Everything came out of one original energy event. Eric Jantsch, Austrian-born American astrophysicist and systems thinker has written that life no longer appears as a thin superstructure over a lifeless physical reality, but as an inherent principle of the dynamics of the universe. The heart of this "New Story" is to celebrate the discovery that everything is a shaping of the same energy that erupted into the universe as the primeval fireball. It is a shaping that has occurred over the millennia of the universe story. Everything in the universe is the result of the emergent process.[14]

The circles and oblongs in the dark background of the painting "The Magnificent Cosmos" (*p.19*) are galaxies within the Hubble Deep Field. They became visible for the first time in 1995, thanks to the remarkable photographs taken from outer space by the Hubble telescope. Focused on a part of the sky that is dark to earth-bound telescopes, the Hubble telescope took exposures over ten days. The telescope captured the faint light from countless, previously unseen distant galaxies which are represented in the collage as small spheres and oblongs in the dark sky. Astronomers now estimate 200 billion galaxies, each with 100 billion stars. We can tell the story of our origins in one continuous narrative extending back into the time when galaxies were formed and even before. Although as a biology student I had studied many details about the evolution of the many species of Earth, I had not known that the origins of Earth, all people and its many beings extended into the long, long history of the universe before early invertebrates, plants and animals left a fossil record on Earth. I find that it offers a certain grandeur and value to every person and to the natural world to understand that we have arisen out of such an unfathomably long creative process.

The Magnificent Cosmos

One of the reasons for the importance of this new evolutionary story for me has been to leave behind the dualism in which matter was inert and changes must be caused by an external force or by random events. As described in the next chapter, matter is not what we have thought in our dualistic, materialistic world. Most remarkably, science itself has transformed our understanding of the nature of matter and of consciousness.

The story of the shaping of the single energy[15] event invites us to think freshly about our identity as earth beings. During those evenings at the church on Central Park West, I began to understand that the ongoing changes and ongoing emergence in evolution is inner to the nature of the cosmos. A number of people have proposed that the early universe has had a latent form of consciousness from the beginning. Furthermore, there is an inner ordering (self-organizing) that explains, at least in part, the emergence of the complexity of Earth and its many beings. It is an emergence that includes a dimension of consciousness from the beginning. The emergent process means that matter, life, and mind are the results of the evolutionary process.[16]

There is no appeal to an external source, but to fundamental dimensions of the universe itself to understand the evolutionary story. The ongoing emergence includes the emergence of all the capacities of the person, mind, soul, psyche, and personal consciousness. With all these comes the emergence of greater agency and self-awareness in living beings. This means that everyone's spiritual journey, in its inner and outer expressions, has become an intrinsic part of the evolutionary story. "Just as we see the unified functioning of particular organisms, so too Earth itself is governed by a unified principle in and through which the total complex of earthly phenomena takes shape."[17] Collectively the story is like a symphony.

Emergence of Human Beings

When I first learned our 13.8 billion-year origin story, I could not fathom how human beings and other animals and plants could possibly have emerged within this greatly expanded new origin story. How did the particles of the early universe evolve into extraordinarily complex, conscious beings like us? Until recent decades, studies of human origins were limited to the changes in living beings on the surface of Earth from whom a line of descent could be traced. This familiar focus of the study of evolution is vastly different from trying to grasp how to trace our origins within the new 13.8-billion-year cosmic origin story. Can we actually trace our origins to a continuous, unbroken succession of events going back to the formation of atoms in stars and before? How are we to understand the emergent process? How did the complex forms of the early beings of Earth and the forms of our bodies arise? I was fortunate to live near Thomas Berry's Riverdale Center for Religious Research so I could attend meetings of the American Teilhard Association held there. After one meeting I asked Thomas Berry about the origin of complex forms in the evolutionary process. He recommended that I read Eric Jantsch's *Self Organizing Universe*.

Self-Organizing and Soul

By reading Jantsch's book with great care and arguing with the librarian about keeping it too long, I began to grasp ideas about the origin of complexity by means of the active, creative ordering powers intrinsic to the cosmos and Earth. Everything is a form that arises in this process, including atoms and cells and human beings. So is a star and the flame of a candle. Self-organizing involves an ordering from within, an inner ordering and, creative patterning such that the universe continually seeks new domains of emergence. New forms of being are carried

The Great Red Oak
This magnificent old red oak stood on the banks of the Hudson River in the yard next to Thomas Berry's Riverdale Center.

forward and are sometimes nested in more complex forms in which self-organizing continues. Parts organize themselves into patterns that could not be predicted from the parts alone. Arthur Peacocke proposes that chaotic processes and self-organizing acting together may produce new patterns and forms.[18]

Thomas Berry and Brian Swimme write that intelligent ordering permeates each being at all levels of complexity. In this understanding nothing exists outside unseen shaping activity.[19] F. David Peat, physicist and speculative thinker, similarly proposed that the generative, ordering power in the universe cannot lie within our familiar mental or material worlds alone, a topic explored in the next chapter. Peat suggested the name "objective intelligence" or "creative ordering" for the generative power that brings about the dynamic ordering of matter and mind.[20] The base of the universe seethes with creativity.[21] Thomas Berry wrote: "The universe emerged into being by a creativity beyond anything we can imagine, a world that assumed its present form by an unpredictable, self-organizing power. What is truly amazing is that these unpredictable processes ... produced a universe so coherent in its structure and so finely ordered in its functioning amid the turbulence of an awesome and relentless inner creative energy."[22]

It was especially important to me to learn, as suggested by the Jungian analyst Michael Comforti, that Jung's archetypes are the psychological parallel to the scientific theory of self-organizing dynamics in nature.[23] So, the archetype of the Self, the soul-like inner ordering of the person, is one example of the inner creative ordering process of Earth and cosmos. Through understanding the nature of self-organizing we can see how archetypal patterns in the depth of consciousness enable a person's participation in the unfolding story. Our psychological patterns are integrated into our new origin story. These patterns are understood by C.G. Jung to be psychoid, which means they order the whole spectrum of our being, including the spiritual, psychological and the physical aspects of our person. This inner creative patterning within us imbeds us fully in Earth and universe so we can embrace a profound depth of belonging as earth beings and as participants in the unfolding story.

The Person as Subject in the Evolutionary Context

Thomas Berry describes three central governing tendencies of evolution that have been identified, given that we now have the perspective of the 4.6-billion-year evolutionary story of Earth:

1) Differentiation: diversity, complexity, multiform nature, heterogeneity;

2) Subjectivity: interiority, greater variety and intensity in psychic modes of expression, presence, self-manifestation, autopoiesis, sentience;

3) Communion: interdependence, internal relatedness, mutuality, interconnectivity, kinship, affiliation, more intimate bonding.

Berry teaches that these three governing tendencies describe the basal intentionality of the universe, as they mold the process of the emergence of contemporary consciousness.[24] They are expressions of the self-organizing and other ordering dimensions of the universe. They are fundamental to the integration of the person into the story.

Identifying these governing principles is of great value because they are occurring below the level of our daily ego-conscious awareness. It is evolution occurring on the inside as they involve the depths of consciousness, the depth of our interiority as well as occurring on the outside with the development of the human person and our cultures. We are warned by Bede Griffiths that "our present conscious mind is still very limited and beneath the conscious mind are all the manifold levels of what is called the unconscious, or better, the subconscious mind."[25] I will return to these ordering tendencies, particularly our subjectivity, in the last chapter.

When I asked Thomas Berry how to understand the emergence of the human person within the long, unfolding story, I don't think I realized the full import of the question. In our world there is an observed movement within the perspective of millions of years of evolutionary history, an increase in subjectivity, communion and differentiation. This view is profoundly different from the reductive, random worldview that dominated much of the West in the last century. In this understanding there is a deep, inner ordering, the self-organizing. No wonder it is very exciting to study the new evolutionary story! It offers a home with a profound given depth of belonging, whether we are conscious of it or not. Thomas Berry writes that "we are quintessentially integral to the universe."[26]

It is urgent that we embrace our understanding of the person within our new origin story and the breakthroughs in our understanding of matter, which are discussed in the next chapter. A transformed future can emerge as our remarkable human identity is embraced and understood. It has been struggling to be born over centuries. Historically, it has been important to keep science and spirituality carefully distinguished to avoid the restrictions that religions sometimes have placed on scientific inquiry. But now, keeping them completely separate would tragically narrow our self-understanding and suppress insights into pathways for the human/Earth future.

The origin story told by a culture molds the community's identity. There is reason to be hopeful that our most remarkable origin story will help transform human self-understanding, awakening us to the inestimable value of Earth and its inhabitants and increase our awareness of the common origin of all human beings and our common destiny. Instead of thinking of the universe as a background in which we exist, we realize we are an integral form of it, one with the continually emerging totality. We learn, Brian Swimme writes, that "we are enveloped by a universe that is a single energetic event, a whole, a unified, multiform, and glorious outpouring of being."[27]

Everything came out of one original energy event. Eric Jantsch has written that life no longer appears as a thin superstructure over a lifeless physical reality, but an inherent principle of the dynamics of the universe. The heart of the new story is to celebrate the discovery that everything is a shaping of the same energy that erupted into the universe at the primeval fireball. It is a shaping that has occurred over the millennia. Everything in the universe is the result of the emergent process.

Reimagining Our Identity

The chapters that follow seek to enable us to enter our new, healing worldview. It is a worldview based primarily on the remarkable breakthrough discoveries made unexpectedly by scientists, and integrated with many traditional and contemporary great voices of mystics. As John Haught describes, a culture without an assumption of intrinsic values integral to the natural world and to individuals as self-aware subjects has made people vulnerable to being manipulated as mere technological objects for political power and economic gain.[28]

The implications of our new origin story called to my mind an experience as a college student in an invertebrate zoology class in Woods Hole, Massachusetts. The inspiration for the painting, "Hydra and Other Sea Creatures" came when I was scuba diving to observe the creatures living immersed in the ocean water on pilings. A colony of small, delicate, nearly transparent hydra caught my attention. At the top of each creature's small, tubular body, around the "mouth", there was a circle of thin tentacles that waved slowly in the currents. I was struck by the physical fragility of the hydra. Furthermore, the colony of hydra was attached to the piling, immobile and seemingly helpless. Suddenly I realized they were not helpless within the embrace of the ocean. They were sustained within the ocean in which they were held and were able to absorb oxygen and catch floating food particles. The hydra are like the lilies of the field we are invited in Matthew 6:28 to consider "how they grow; they neither toil nor spin."

Hydra and Other Sea Creatures

Chapter Two
A Transformed Understanding of Matter

A mazingly, it is physicists who have broken wide open the narrow, objectified worldview so dominant in much of our culture. We are invited to reconsider and reimagine several often taken-for-granted assumptions in the face of most surprising, impressive discoveries made in the last two centuries by physicists. Insights into the nature of matter can help us find an understanding of Earth and its many beings that offer a major opening for our embrace of a profound spiritual identity. It is an identity that deepens our individual subjectivity and at the same time supports a re-visioning of the natural world and a more profound communion with Earth and with each other. It takes time and careful thought to digest the fundamental changes now offered to us.

We cannot allow ourselves to be intimidated by the reputation of physics we may have acquired in high school that it is entirely obscure and difficult. If we ignore its discoveries, we will miss insights of great importance. We need to hear the unexpected news of the remarkable hidden energetic interiority of the physical world which includes, of course, the interiority of our very person and the entirety of the natural world. It may be a slow process for the new insights to have meaning so they can speak to us directly, addressing, challenging, and transforming our everyday, taken-for-granted assumptions. To grasp the enormity of the changes in our conception of matter, the very stuff of our bodies and the natural world, a bit of history will be helpful.

The reader will have understood from the first chapter that these pages are in part an inquiry into understanding mystical experience. To many people it will not be immediately obvious why it is important, given this focus, to explore the breakthroughs in physics. Perhaps they have thought of mysticism as concerned with other-worldly questions. However,

26

it is because physicists have recognized a hidden energetic reality within and around our daily world that the work of physicists is of concern to understanding mysticism. There is an understanding in spiritual traditions throughout the world that identifies the nature of spirit that can help us hear the significance of the physicist's recent breakthroughs.

Sam Mackintosh, a teacher with a life-long interest in the convergence of science and religion, writes that spirit comes from the Latin word spiritus, a word for power and energy. Spiritus is related to similar words such as, "chi" in Chinese, "pneuma" in Greek, "prana" in Hindi, "ruah" in Hebrew, "vayu" in ancient Persian and "wonuya" in Lakota. They all have the same basic meaning of the dynamic and life-giving energy of the universe. Mackintosh writes, "Essentially spiritus is the power and energy of the universe at work here and now in the natural world and in ourselves. Spiritus pervades the whole of reality from the most elementary wave-particles, atoms and molecules to the most complex beings."[29]

This understanding of the meaning of spiritus grounds its meaning in our daily world, so spirit is not understood to arise from above or outside our world. It is a foundation for hearing freshly the mystics' words and the discoveries of the physicists. It can help us have greater confidence and understanding of spiritual experience and its availability within our lives. When I learned about this meaning of spiritus, my experience of being knelt, came rushing to my mind as an energetic interiority expressing itself in the kneeling.

A Brief Episode in Nineteenth Century Physics

In the early nineteenth century, Michael Faraday, an impoverished Londoner without formal education, was working in a laboratory that was exploring how magnets and various electrically charged objects attract and repel each other. The physicist Carlo Rovelli explains in his book, *Reality Is Not What It Seems*[30] that Faraday assumed in the context of the understanding of the day, based on physics derived from Newton, that the space between the magnets was empty so the reason that oppositely charged magnets attracted each other was because of some quality of the magnets themselves. As Faraday worked with the magnets and charged electrical objects "by his hands, in close contact with these objects, he is led to an intuition that will become the basis of modern physics. He 'sees' something new."[31] He "sees" that the magnetic objects do not attract or repel each other directly through empty space as was supposed. Instead they interact "only via the medium interposed between them." The space between the magnets is not empty! It was an intuitive insight, a kind of inspiration. Faraday was conscious that he was suggesting nothing less than a modification of the structure of the world.[33]

The space between the magnets subsequently became known as a "field". Faraday and James Maxwell, who wrote the equations describing the discovery, have "replaced the idea of a 'force' with a 'force field.'"[34] This statement by Fritjof Capra will become important as we try to grasp the nature of fields. The attraction between the magnetic objects occurs by means of the field. Faraday intuited a medium between the magnets and this developed eventually into the recognition of not only this medium which is now identified as the electro-magnetic field, but also other fields have been identified, including the gravitational field.

These fields are everywhere diffused throughout space and time. I have retold the story of Faraday's insight because it so dramatically helps us appreciate the great changes in our understanding of the space around us, between us, and the space within all atoms and therefore within ourselves. Our worldview has been turned upside down when compared to the objectified world I studied in college.

The Non-Visible Realm of Fields

The identification of the electromagnetic and gravitational fields, and discoveries about the atom have all led to the recognition of a universal quantum field. Early names for this include "the universal field of quantum mechanics", "the false vacuum", and "the universal wave function." This universal quantum field was hypothesized in the 1920s and experimentally verified in the 1940s. The name proposed by Brian Swimme for all the fields now identified is the "all-nourishing abyss". He describes it as a non-visible ocean of potentiality. It is a realm of non-material power, an empty fullness.[35] Another name is "seamless plenum", a metaphorical term for the quantum field, which is based on the description of the nonvisible interior realm being interconnected (seamless) and a highly energetic ocean of potentiality (a plenum).[36] This use of a common generic name does not deny the importance of the specific expressions of the fields that have been identified, like the gravitational field and the fields involved in the formation of the atom; it is a generic term that names the hidden energetic ground that physicists have identified. The phrase "seamless plenum" is used in these pages.

Carlo Rovelli is another important voice pointing to the vast non-visible interiority of our daily world.[37] He describes the effort by physicists to integrate general relativity (which addresses the large-scale nature of space and time) and quantum theory (which addresses the nature and behavior of matter and energy on the atomic and subatomic level). He concludes his review of these efforts to find a comprehensive field addressing this search with a proposal of "covariant quantum fields." It is a proposal that has its origins in the story of Faraday's insight that the space between the magnets is not empty. Rovelli's proposal is as follows: "The substance of which the world is made has been radically simplified in recent years. The world, particles, light, energy, space, and time – all of this is nothing but the manifestation of a single type of entity: covariant quantum fields."[38] This is a startling statement that certainly attracts attention. Rovelli's proposal that the world is "nothing but a single type of entity" the covariant quantum fields and Brian Swimme's use of the phrase the "all-nourishing abyss" both address a comprehensive field that has changed the world of physics and cannot be ignored by all of us non-physicists. The world of science was transformed from within.

The nonvisible, seamless plenum, is profoundly real and powerful. It is not a thing, not even "strictly speaking, a physical space but rather a power that gives birth and that absorbs existence at a thing's annihilation. ... Each particular thing is directly and essentially grounded in the all-nourishing abyss."[39] Swimme continues: "The foundational reality of the universe is this unseen ocean of potentiality."[40] He writes that "knowledge of the all-nourishing abyss is the beginning of a process that reaches its fulfillment in direct experience."[41]

The Seamless Plenum Is Highly Energetic

Physicist and author Fred Alan Wolf identifies the seamless plenum as the non-visible, non-visualizable quantum field, which is highly energetic. However, that energy cannot be measured directly by the scientific methods of measurement used in our daily world of space and time. The use of the word energy can be misleading as the energy of the seamless plenum is not of the same nature as the energy measured in our space-time world.

"We know that particles actually pop up out of the seamless plenum, although the particles usually annihilate each other. This shows the ceaseless generativity of the seamless plenum, a realm of very great power. The vast nonvisible realm is a fullness as being arises as out of a field of fecund emptiness."[42] This is a moving discovery as the seamless plenum is intrinsic to our being.

Ralph Waldo Emerson wrote that "What lies behind us and what lies before us are tiny matters compared to what lies within us." Brian Swimme writes that if all the individual things of the universe were to evaporate, one would be left with an infinity of pure generative power.[43]

Now there is a significant divergence of opinion among physicists about estimating this generative power based on how it is measured and assumptions about how it is to be identified. However, what was initially misnamed a vacuum is powerful, not empty. The seamless plenum is not a place; it is a power. Here is one description of how the energy is measured:

"The way to estimate its energy is to measure the amount of energy in fluctuations from the quantum vacuum in the space of a cubic centimeter, which results in the enormous figure of 10^{94} grams of matter. This figure is based on the mass-energy equivalence in the famous formula of Einstein, e=mc2. The result of this measurement is sometimes described as an infinite amount of energy."[44]

There are further reflections in the next chapter about the nature of the seamless plenum from sources other than physics, namely from mysticism.

Our Daily, Physical World

We have all learned that matter of our bodies and the world around us is composed of atoms. During the early part of the 20th century major developments in our understanding of the atom emerged. Physicists tell us that atoms that comprise the matter of our daily world are patterns of energy formed within the quantum field. Since the atom is a pattern of energy, everything including our bodies, is patterns of energy.

This is an unsuspected understanding of matter compared to our assumption that the atom is made of particles, the nucleus and the electrons whirling around it. It is a discovery based on study by physicists of the hidden, nonvisible nature of the quantum fields that comprise the atom and the pattern of energy that has taken form within it to form the atom.

We can no long assume the atom is comprised of particulate pieces of matter. The basic structure of the atom, a pattern of energy, formed early in the evolutionary story with the creation of hydrogen. All the hydrogen of our world was formed as the universe cooled, an estimated 380,000 years after the "big bang." This is the only time hydrogen was created. As the evolutionary story tells us, the heavier elements formed later in large stars. Brian Swimme teaches that if you leave hydrogen gas alone it becomes birds and butterflies and all of our daily world.

Within the atoms there are, in addition to the nucleus, quarks and gluons and electrons; these particles have been discovered to be very small knots of energy (quanta), compressed energy events that sometimes are particle-like, although with no dimensions and sometimes spread out as waves. When involved in an interaction, waves take on a "particulate" form, but the "particles" are actually an energy constellation.

We are presented with a profound change in worldview with the recognition that the atoms of our daily manifest world have risen within the seamless plenum, initially as just mentioned, with the formation of hydrogen. I was startled when watching Brains Swimme's video, *Canticle to the Cosmos*, years ago, to learn the image of the baseball diamond to illustrate the "emptiness" of the atom. The electrons we were told would be like a homerun ball high above the stadium if the nucleus is imagined to be a ball sitting on the pitcher's mound.

We've been told, as previously mentioned, the seamless plenum is 99.99% of the atom. This figure is disputed, not because it is too big, but because the percentage depends on a number of assumptions about one's understanding of the emergence and disappearance of the electrons and the nature of the nucleus. Some physicists tell us the atom is comprised entirely of the energy in the quantum field as the electrons and other "particles" are energy patterns of that field not to be separated out of the seamless plenum.[45]

The seamless plenum is not only within the atom and consequently within our bodies, but it is also right in front of us and around us, even where there is no physical object and we might assume there is only empty space. If all the atoms and molecules of the atmosphere, the subatomic particles of matter and the radioactivity were removed from the space in front of us, it is still not empty as the seamless plenum is present.[46] This includes the gravitational field that we know is also between us and the sun and all the celestial bodies. The seamless plenum is everywhere.

An invitation to ponder freshly the nature of our bodies and the natural world, is offered by Duane Elgin, a writer concerned with evoking collective awakening. He teaches that the entire universe is maintained moment by moment by an unbroken flow-through of energy. He also says the world is a set of variously integrated clusters of vibrations; he explains that matter dissolves into knots of energy. Ervin Laszlo says something similar.

According to Elgin, no particle stands in existence in a completely independent manner cut off from the seamless plenum. I find this truly remarkable! Here is the foundation of a deep physical belonging within the non-visualizable dimension of our new cosmic origin story. For science this is a new world although as we will see, it is not so new in some spiritual traditions. It seems to me to be of fundamental importance for the individual to be informed about the energetic nature of matter (clusters of vibrations) and to recognize the discovery of the non-visualizable source within which the clusters take form to become manifest as our daily physical world!

There are a number of voices supporting this basic insight into the nature of matter. The physicist David Bohm conceived of matter as relatively autonomous excitation patterns that are inseparable from the deeper level.[47] K.C. Cole writes in the book, *A Hole in the Universe,* that matter itself is only the energetic geometry of forces in empty space.[48]

The painting "Everything Has A Within" is a celebration of the invitation to abandon the crippling reductive world, however grateful I am that airplanes fly reliably, and my car will run if it has enough gasoline. The nature of the nonvisible interiority of the physical world is suggested by the marbled paper in the background to the painting "Everything Has A Within." Actually,

Everything Has a Within

this depiction the interiority of matter with marbled paper may not be appropriate as, because the seamless plenum is non-visualizable. However, the marbled paper can be understood to suggest the mysterious nature of the seamless plenum and the recognition that it is highly energetic, and that it can be known experientially, at least in part, even though it is not visualizable. Suddenly, at the very core of science, there is a profound mystery.

It is an Epochal Change

The transformative discovery that matter is patterns of energy formed in the quantum field (seamless plenum), tells us of the non-visible interiority (seamless plenum) of our everyday physical world. The phrase from Carlo Rovelli telling us of "quantum fields whose elementary events happen in spacetime"[49] is very helpful as it is holding together the nonvisible quantum fields (seamless plenum) and the patterns of energy, the elementary events, that form the atoms that comprise our daily manifest world. They are inseparable.

Matter is certainly not what we have thought. We are indeed living in a time of radical change. This discovery of the nature of matter is central to our new understanding of our everyday daily world as it does not allow us to separate our daily manifest physical world from its source. The source is throughout the manifest world as the clusters of vibrations or patterns of energy form within it. The nonvisible seamless plenum and the manifest world cannot be separated into two distinct domains. This intimacy of the non-visible generative realm, the seamless plenum, and our manifest daily world is a transformative discovery as it is coming from physics. Our self-understanding is profoundly changed. We can imagine the seamless plenum permeating the entirety of our very being.

In the next chapter we will explore the amazing discovery of the nature of the seamless plenum in relation to the people's words about their felt experiences of the depth of consciousness.

Connecting These Discoveries to the Big Bang

It is natural to ask how these discoveries about matter can be integrated with the 13.8 billion years' story of our origins and with ideas about the cosmic flaring forth at the beginning of time. Do the discoveries of the seamless plenum help integrate us into our cosmic origin story? Here is what Brian Swimme and Thomas Berry write about this important question in their book, *The Universe Story*.

"Originating power brought forth a universe. All the energy that would ever exist in the entire course of time, erupted as a single quantum – a singular gift – existence. ... There was no place in the universe that was separate from the originating power of the universe. Each thing of the universe had its very roots in this realm. Even space-time itself was a tossing, churning, foaming out of the originating reality, instant by instant. Each of the sextillion particles that foamed into existence had its root in this quantum vacuum, the originating reality. ... Though the originating power gave birth to the universe fifteen billion years ago, this realm of power is not simply located there at that point of time, but is rather a condition of every moment of the universe, past, present and to come."[50]

This is a fundamentally revelatory understanding of our origins as Swimme and Berry have integrated the discoveries about the interiority of matter just described in this chapter, with the larger origin story about the beginning of the cosmos. They identify the seamless plenum (quantum vacuum), the very inner ongoing creative power within all of us, now integral to the complex physical world developed over the billions of years, as the origin of the Big Bang. This immanent creative power is the foundation of the ongoing creativity of the universe described in the evolutionary story that has brought forth complex beings, human beings included. This process has come to include contemporary scientists themselves who have been able to identify this originating reality and as was just described, it is integral to our being.

Reality Is Inherently Omni-centered

Another discovery central to the cosmic origin story and human identity is recognizing the nature of the expansion of the universe. As the cosmos expanded and continues to expand, there is no place in the universe separate from the originating center, instant by instant. We have to avoid the image that the universe began with an explosion after which pieces are imagined as being thrown away from the place of the explosion. Instead, due to the manner of expansion, the universe is understood to be omni-centered. The famous image of the expanding dough with raisins in it, helps us grasp the nature of omni-centricity. Space emerges or stretches between the supercluster of galaxies represented by the raisins. The raisins do not move farther away from the center as happens in an explosion here on Earth. This means that each of us is at this moment at the very center of the universe. Given the nature of matter and the interiority of matter, we are the realm that gives birth to the universe; each of us is at the center of our omni-centered universe where the universe came into being.[51] Brian Swimme writes: "Each person is situated in that very place and is rooted in that very power, that brought forth all the matter and energy of the universe."[52] We certainly have to ponder that!

Non-locality

There has been another discovery that may further change our assumptions about the nature of our daily world. It challenges us to question the predictable world of space and time that was thought to be fully explanatory of life. In the mechanistic understanding of the world, it was assumed that two things communicate by means of touching or by a signal of some kind, like a sound wave coming to our ears or the wind carrying a leaf to our feet. Non-locality refers to a profoundly different interconnection. According to the non-locality proposed by quantum physicists, local order (such as the spin of the particles in an atom) in our daily space-time world is affected by phenomena that are faster than light.[53] The prediction was made by quantum physics that entangled electrons sharing the same wavelength would snap into opposite spins instantaneously no matter how far apart they are. Such a mode of connection was thought impossible in our understanding of time and space in our 19th century traditional world.

The experiment to test the proposal that there is unmediated connection (that there is no touching or no signal) involved a pair of coupled electrons, also called "entangled electrons," that have opposite spin. Tested in the early 1980s by physicist Alain Aspect, and subsequently verified many times, it was found that in fact this instantaneous change does occur. When one particle takes one spin, the other instantaneously takes the opposite spin, no matter how far apart they are. To the shock and surprise of many, including Einstein, the change in the spin of entangled particles is not caused by some force in the daily physical space-time world of objects; it is not mediated within the classic understanding of space and time in our daily world.[54] The fastest mode of communication, that is the fastest signal, in our daily world is the speed of light, but in as much as the change in the entangled particles is instantaneous it cannot have been mediated by a signal in our daily world.[55]

Non-locality is fascinating but it is still little understood. In a conversation Steve Martin, a physicist and teacher, noted that entanglement happens only in certain carefully prepared situations. Many people extrapolate to say that entanglement implies a universal oneness or unity, but it is still a mystery about why we observe this entanglement only in certain circumstances and not everywhere. Yet it is understood that quantum theory is not a local theory. This is a topic of great interest to pay attention to as further studies are undertaken.

An Inclusive Image

A helpful image to summarize our understanding of the world given the radical discoveries by physicists is offered by Sir James Jeans, a British physicist and mathematician. He suggested that we think of the world that we see with our senses as the "outer surface of nature, like the surface of a deep flowing stream." He said that material objects have origins that go "deep down into the stream." This nonvisible realm inside the stream is quite complex, filled, with fields and patterns and as yet largely undescribed "energies" and dimensions.

Drawing on the insights and the language of the new story, Herman Greene, founder of the Center for Ecozoic Studies, writes that "there is unity within the incredible complexity and diversity of the universe and our planet is a surprise and mystery. It cannot be accounted for simply by mechanical forces or even digital calculations of the most advanced kind. It is analogous to the unity with which our body functions and also our consciousness which is embodied but not located in any particular part of our body. We, our history, our Earth, are part of the universe, just as any member of our body is part of our body."[56]

We are more alive and filled with dynamic energy than most of us have known. Do we have conscious experience of this hidden dimension of the world? This is the topic of inquiry in the next chapter. We are all offered a larger more comprehensive identity than an identity circumscribed by suffering and an objectified worldview.

Consciousness

This energetic interiority of our person has been of great interest to me because a door opened to an understanding of that awakening experience, the strange energetic knowing that came to consciousness as I was knelt now many years ago in the bedroom. The words of many mystics we will look at in the next chapter can be heard freshly in our new context. Furthermore, the changes are of great interest because they speak to our often wanton, ill-considered destruction of the natural world as we have not recognized the fullness of its being.

Several people have come to understand that both matter and consciousness arise in the seamless plenum, the hidden dimension of our identity and that of the natural world. David Bohm thought that the mind side of things and the matter side of things have a common origin in the "implicate order", a name referring to the nonvisible interiority of the world that is understood in a way that is comparable to the understanding of the seamless plenum. We have identified the seamless plenum as a hidden dimension of the manifest world within which matter and consciousness unfold simultaneously.

Matter is now understood to be taking form within the seamless plenum. This understanding of the formation of matter opens the door to understanding mystical experience, as both matter and consciousness have their origin in the seamless plenum. We learn that the seamless plenum is not to be separated from the manifest as the manifest is taking the form of the plenum. The relationship of this interiority to the experiences of mystics is discussed and pursued in the next chapter. Recall that spirit (prana, ruah) is recognized worldwide as the implicit energy, the dynamic and life-giving energy of the universe. Isn't mysticism an awareness of spirit, if spirit is understood in this integrated sense? In the next chapter it is proposed that mysticism is a felt awareness of the energy of the seamless plenum that is integral to, thus cannot be separated from the patterns of energy that comprise the matter of our daily world. Is the witness of mystics finding a home in which its witness takes on great significance? In our contemporary context, we will consider freshly the claim of a remarkable identity for the human person as the fullness of human identity is embraced and lived.

CHAPTER THREE
Listening to Mystics' Words in the Context of the Radical Discoveries by Physicists

Our radically transformed understanding of matter offers a most heartening context in which to listen with our new assumptions to the words and the lives of the contemplatives and the mystics. When I first began learning about the unexpected discoveries made by physicists, I was deeply moved and excited. It is now possible, to our amazement, that the insights of mystics that have too often seemed obscure, requiring a leap of faith, can be heard freshly as integral to the worldview now offered by physicists! To our delight and amazement, we propose in this chapter to listen to the mystics' words in our new context.

Mystics' Witness Across Many Traditions

Many people will be aware that often the witness of mystics has not been readily accepted nor central to religious institutions. However, one reason to listen to them is how surprising and unexpected it is to find the persistence of witnesses to mystical union in the three monotheistic faiths since each in their classical expression is based upon a clear and unsurmountable distinction between God and man.[57] Yet there is a mystical tradition in all three faiths. This suggests the fundamental importance and compelling nature of the experience, given this persistent witness in the face of opposition. As Louis Dupré observes, we have to consider carefully the specific nature of mystical union.[58]

When reading the words of the mystics that follow, the reader is invited to listen to them in the context of our discovery of the seamless plenum and our transformed understanding of matter. As we listen to the words of the mystics in the context of the discoveries about matter, it is important to keep in mind that the individual mystics who wrote these words were, of course, integral to the unfolding evolutionary story, although that may or may not have been part of the knowledge of their culture.

The sentences that follow are the words that the individuals quoted used to describe what they have come to know and understand about their identity and that of the world around them. I begin with the words of those individuals who, in these particular selections, do not use the word "God".

"There is in all things an inexhaustible sweetness and purity ... [that] flows to me from the unseen roots of all created being." —Thomas Merton[59]

"The spirit is the invisible aspect of matter and matter is the visible aspect of spirit." —C.G. Jung[60]

"A mystic has found a way of seeing the finite, namely as it exists within the infinite." —Louis Dupré[61]

"My place is the placeless." —Rumi[62]

"The Diaphany of the Divine at the heart of a glowing Universe – as I have experienced it through contact with the earth – the Divine radiating from the depths of a blazing Matter... " —Teilhard de Chardin[63]

"The time is fulfilled, and the Kingdom of Heaven is at hand..." -Jesus of Nazareth: *Mark* 1:15

Some mystics describe their experience using the word "God." In recent centuries, the word "God" has too often been heard as being about a reality that is other to our being, not within our very person nor within the natural world. This is not surprising given the objectification of the natural world by science and the teachings that each of the three monotheistic faiths in their classical expression, are based upon a clear and unsurmountable distinction between God and man.

Some readers may object to the use of the word "God", because they recognize that the traditional separation that the word "God" may carry is no longer appropriate in the context of the discovery of our 13.8-billion-year evolutionary story and the discoveries about the nature of matter. The word "God" will not be used in the discussions in these pages to avoid the assumption of deep dualism that the word can carry in the West. Yet we cannot neglect the remarkable words offered by many mystics who often had understandings of the word "God" in ways that are compatible with our emerging worldview. Their words invite attention given their experiential basis and we must be aware that we cannot assume what each person understood about the nature of God as many wrote before the separation of the sacred from matter that became quite dominant in the West in recent centuries.

God "is in everything," writes Julian. God is "nature's substance," the very essence of life. —Julian of Norwich[64]

"...the consensus of the mystics of all living religions, namely that God is nearest me in me, that God is the very Self of my self, and that we are all members of one Godbody, who is the very ground of our being." —John Yungblut[65]

"My me is God, nor do I know my selfhood save in Him." —Catherine of Genoa[66]

"To comprehend and understand God as he is in himself, above and beyond all likeness, is to be God with God, without intermediary." —Jan van Ruusbroec[67]

"As I have often said, there is something in the soul so closely akin to God that it is already one with him and need never be united to him." —Meister Eckhart[68]

"To God's magnificent masquerade as us." —Hafiz[69]

"Verily, all is Brahman." —The ancient teaching of the Upanishads. "Brahman" means "God" in Sanskrit.

You are filled with the utter fullness of God. —*Ephesians* 3:19

In these words, there is clearly a strong, repeated testimony based on the experience of these individuals that tell us of an unexpected human identity. But as discussed in the following pages, it needs no longer be so unexpected in the context of our transformed understanding of matter.

Are Physicists and Mystics Touching on the Same Non-visible Dimension?

We are given pause for serious thought, even shock, when we recognize the apparent coincidence of the testimony of mystics to "invisible fecundity", to use Thomas Merton's words, and the discovery by physicists of the nonvisible, nonmaterial quantum field. It is the living person, the mystic, who has told us they have experienced invisible fecundity. Since the living person is

the complexification over evolutionary time of the patterns of
energy formed within the quantum field, we can grasp that the
mystic may experience the quantum field, the nonvisible field,
the seamless plenum that in the example from Merton is called
the "invisible fecundity." Our daily ego consciousness does not
have the capacity to know the "invisible fecundity" but there
is a knowing/consciousness integral to the Self/soul, the self-
organizing, formative inner pattern of the person. Are physicists
and mystics touching into the same hidden dimension? Is
there a most remarkable recognition of the hidden, nonvisible
interiority by two distinct modes of inquiry?

And we must remember the seamless plenum is not a place
or a thing but, as described by physicists, a field within which
patterns of energy emerge that are the manifest world. It is with
the senses and daily consciousness that these patterns become
known. Mystics tell us there is another mode of knowing the
nature of the world of which we are a part.

In response to Catherine of Genoa saying "My me is God,"
many people have thought her words are foolish because their
ideas of God do not allow this. Perhaps they have assumed the
person's physical body and its abilities and the individual's daily
consciousness and emotions fully describe the individual. Now,
given the discovery of the seamless plenum or quantum field
we know from physics that the person is not fully identified by
describing the individual's physical and mental characteristics
in our daily space-time world. Now we know from physicists
that there is a nonvisible dimension of our person, the quantum
field.

The patterns of energy comprising the manifest world
emerged in the quantum field. Integrating the discoveries from
physics with the experiences of the mystics suggests that when
Catherine of Genoa wrote "my me is God," she is experiencing
the seamless plenum. She experienced a mode of awareness/
consciousness, a mode of knowing, the nonvisible foundation
of her being, which is integral to the complex energetic patterns
of her daily person organized by the Self/soul of her person.
This integrates the seamless plenum of the physicists with the
experiences of the mystics. The Self as used here is the unseen
shaping dynamism, a self-organizing pattern that is constitutive
of living beings. As the Self is grounded in the seamless plenum,
the seamless plenum is present in a numinous form of knowing

integral to the Self. It is not the full energy of the seamless plenum that is known, but that which is known within the complex energetic patterns of the person. We are compelled to pay attention to the remarkable coincidence of insight into a hidden dimension of our being central to our identity.

Hidden But Now Recognized

There are many reasons why it is of fundamental importance to pay careful attention to this common witness. Both traditions point to a non-material, non-visible dimension of the world that is hidden to daily consciousness and modes of knowing in our daily space-time world. We have given examples of the witness of many mystics and now, most remarkably, physicists are telling us of a nonvisible dimension of our world!

Brian Swimme writes that the quantum field is neither a material thing nor an energy constellation, yet it is profoundly real and profoundly powerful.[70] Both the mystics and the physicists witness to the discovery of this interiority. Until the last century, physicists did not recognize the quantum field, the seamless plenum, and its presence integral to the patterns of energy that are the matter of our daily world! It is a heartening discovery for the individual who is exploring personal spiritual identity. There is enough coincidence of insight that we find support for the witness of contemplatives and mystics through the ages with regard to their testimony of an actual nonvisible, hidden presence. Listening carefully to their common witness invites fresh reflections about our identity.

The writing of Pierre Teilhard de Chardin offers examples of experience of this interiority. Teilhard de Chardin experienced in childhood and throughout his life what he called a sense of plenitude or "Cosmic sense" at the heart of a glowing universe. In his essay, "The Heart of Matter," he tells us that "the World gradually caught fire for me, burst into flames; how this happened all during my life, and as a result of my whole life, until it formed a great luminous mass, lit from within, that surrounded me."[71] He writes that his experience was so strong that he might have embraced a dualistic world that separated matter and the sacred and he might have chosen to disappear into the formless, abandoning matter, to become the Other. In this manner, he tells us he might have escaped to the spirit world but he recognized spirit at the heart of matter. He wrote that he was saved by an understanding of evolution. Because of evolution he recognized that matter and spirit are no longer two things, but two states or two aspects of one and the same cosmic stuff.[73]

Here are Julian of Norwich's words again: "God is nature's substance." Isn't it natural to ask if her words based on her experience can also be described as an experience of the nonvisible seamless plenum, the quantum field? This proposal should not be heard as limiting her words to the discoveries made by physicists as they do not claim full knowledge of the seamless plenum, including how it could be experienced subjectively. By identifying her experience as the seamless plenum, we are assuming she is conscious of the plenum known to be integral with the patterns of energy that comprise her being as a living person. This proposal needs to be heard in the context of Julian being a complex, living person who is saying these words within our evolutionary cosmos. This commonality of witness simply affirms the need for very careful renewed attention to the many experiences of the mystics, and their recognition of a dimension of human identity too often ignored in our culture. The discovery of the seamless plenum strengthens the mystic's witness and invites us to ponder anew our identity. People will draw forth, in our new context of evolution, new images and insights about human identity and the nature of Earth.

The mystical experiences just offered are only an extremely small sample. There is long historical witness of mystical experience from many traditions east and west, suggesting they are universal in nature, although with much discussed differences in the traditions and their understandings of the experiences.

The Tradition of No-thing-ness

Meister Eckhart and Dionysius the Areopagite refer to a tradition of "No-thing-ness" that is an ongoing creative source of everything. Remarkably physicists, for a period, referred to a "vacuum" of unmeasurable generative power that is the condition of every moment of the universe, past, present and future. The word "vacuum" is no longer used to describe the nonvisible interiority that is now identified as the "seamless plenum." The now outdated word "vacuum" once used by physicists, and the phrase "no-thing-ness" sometimes used by mystics, both recognize that everything in the universe has its roots in a dimension that cannot be studied and measured in the manner by which we identify things in our daily space-time world. It is not a thing. This is a remarkable coincidence of insights, given that both traditions have become aware of the generative power and creative source that is interior to our world but a mystery to our daily modes of knowing. The great wonder is that the empirical, rational journey of science should come to an insight long carried within the spiritual traditions. We are encouraged to no longer project numinous experiences out of ourselves and out of the natural world, and thereby abandon our full identity, devalue the natural world, and fail to seek expression of that reality within our person and our communities.

Physicists Who Witness to this Integration

The common witness of quantum physics and mystics being proposed in these pages will be challenged by some physicists, speaking as physicists, as this proposal lies outside their traditional field of inquiry. Their research as physicists is not concerned with addressing issues of consciousness. However, it has been the intuition of scientists that led to the discovery of the seamless plenum, which shows that the two traditions cannot be kept entirely in distinct silos. Faraday's intuition was the origin of profound changes in physics, as was Einstein's intuition about the nature of gravity.

Werner Heisenberg, one of the creators of quantum theory, has argued that at the deepest level of reality, the ground of the vacuum, there is emptiness, equivalent to what the Buddhists call "sunyata," prior to anything that "is."[74]

In his book *The Tao of Physics*, Fritjof Capra, a theoretical physicist, writes that "modern physics leads us to a view of the world which is very similar to the views held by mystics of all ages and traditions."[75] It is ironic, Capra notes, that physics, the extreme specialization of the rational mind, should be the science that has now led us to mysticism.

Another voice addressing this integration is John Hagelin, a physicist and spiritual seeker. His work as a physicist is with the grand unified field of string theory and also, he is a practitioner and promoter of transcendental meditation (TM). He said that the ocean of pure intelligence or pure consciousness he comes to with TM and the unified field of string theory must be one. Since science is working at the level of the unified field, it is in a position, Hagelin argues, to corroborate the ground of our consciousness and the fundamental unity of people.[76] Ervin Laszlo is an author and former professor of philosophy and systems theory and future studies in the U.S., Europe and the Far East. He works with scientific discoveries in his strong advocacy of the rise of the integral vision of reality. He writes about innovative scientists who lift the private experiences that speak to the integral nature of reality "from the domain of unverifiable intuition into the realm of interpersonally verifiable public knowledge."[77]

A Common Witness to our Hidden Identity

It is confusing that spiritual experiences of such central importance to human identity are at the same time largely hidden to daily consciousness. Given our objectivized worldview, it is no wonder that people have so often thought experience of a numinous reality (the seamless plenum) came from outside themselves. Our emerging worldview based on the affirmation from physics, and from the experience of mystics, of a dimension of our world that is both hidden to daily consciousness and yet central to human identity is an important coincidence of insight. The occasion for the awakening of a mystical experience may be something in the space-time world, outside us, as a forest or mountains, but the felt experience is known within the consciousness of the person.

This commonality of insight is that the mystic's experience of the "invisible fecundity," to use Merton's words, and the physicist's recognition of the nonvisible seamless plenum certainly coincide. Both are witnesses to that which is hidden to daily consciousness, and at the same time central to our very identity.

This comonality is central to spirituality. Catherine of Genoa wrote "my me is God" and John Yungblut wrote "God is the very self of myself."

In physics it is central since the nonvisible seamless plenum, and the energetic pattern of the atom arising in it, are central to our contemporary understanding of the manifest world that we know with our senses.

In spite of the cultural divide between science and religion in the West, the individual inquirer is free to ask if we are encountering a startling and most heartening, life-giving convergence of insight that invites careful attention. It would be a transformative breakthrough for the West, yet by no means entirely new. Many cultures have known of the great importance of the hidden dimension of the physical world. They have not lost knowledge of the sacred depth of the natural world.

Ervin Laszlo describes the Akasha, an element in Hindu cosmology which is the womb from which everything has emerged and into which everything will ultimately re-descend. Laszlo writes: "In the traditional conception Akasha is an all-encompassing medium that underlies all things; the medium that becomes all things. It is real, but so subtle that it cannot be perceived until it becomes the many things that populate the manifest world."[78]

It is the fundamental medium of the cosmos. It underlies all the particles and all the forces and fields that govern particles and the systems built of particles, throughout space and time. Science has a name for it: it is the quantum vacuum (also known as the "unified vacuum" or "neuther").[79] Thus, Laszlo identifies the quantum vacuum with the Akasha. The term "vacuum" is no longer used because it has been discovered that it is not empty. It is the seamless plenum, the all-nourishing abyss, the quantum field.

Teilhard de Chardin offers an image that speaks to the integration just offered: "Like the meridians as they approach the poles, science, philosophy and religions are bound to converge as they draw near to the whole."[80] With this understanding and the compelling literature from around the world, life-changing-mystical experiences can no longer be culturally marginalized to a category of a particular type of human religious consciousness that is not understood to be revelatory of the nature of our daily world and the identity of the person.

Fear of Reductionism

Since this integration draws on the discovery by physicists of the seamless plenum, we may be concerned that once again, as in the recent past, theological traditions will become too influenced by reductive scientific thought. Will important dimensions of traditional theology be reduced by this discovery made by physicists? One response to this, is to be aware that as Philip Clayton points out, science can often be equated with reductionism.[81] Given the nature of what we learned in science classes we easily make this equation. As previously described, I fell victim as a student to its reductive power. However, this danger is certainly not appropriate in this case, because it assumes a false understanding of the nature of the seamless plenum. The charge of reductionism is avoided since the nature of seamless plenum does not allow us to categorize it as part of the reductive inquiry of western science. The quantum field is neither a material thing nor an energy constellation. It is not subject to being known by the traditional objective methods of measurement used by physicists so science itself must deal with a very mysterious reality. One of the specific fears is that there will be a loss of transcendence as we work with this integration. In the next chapter, an understanding of transcendence from the work of Louis Dupré brings one way of thinking of transcendence congruent with this integration. Louis Dupré observed that "following the years of gradual change, the real is no longer an object that reason places before the mind, but rather a totality of which the mind constitutes an integral dynamic part.[82]

The Mystic's Words Can No Longer Be Marginalized

This integration avoids relegating the insights of the contemplatives and mystics to a minority, isolated voice of individual subjective experiences without significance for all of us. To my great surprise, joy, and near disbelief, western people can no longer use outdated mechanistic, materialistic science to deny outright the insights of mystics. Physicists themselves have discovered a hidden, nonvisible depth integral to the manifest, visible world. Recall the meaning of spiritus, the dynamic and life-giving energy of the universe. Isn't it legitimate to propose that the seamless plenum and the patterns of energy arising in it are this spiritus?

We no longer need a leap of faith to value our spiritual awakenings. Now, thanks to breakthroughs in physics, we can joyfully have confidence that the world is permeated with the "invisible fecundity". We are coming to know the invisible fecundity ever more fully. To my great surprise there is a home for mystical experiences in our new emerging understanding of matter, the very matter of our person and all of Earth. Doors have opened widely into a transformed understanding of the world because of breakthroughs in science and because we have access to more accounts of mystical modes of knowing from worldwide sources drawing on the past and continuing in the present.

Teachers from the East have had a great influence here in the United States. It was only in the 20th century that English translations of the work of Jalal al-Din Rumi became available.[83] This recognition of the place of mysticism in our new context can enable us to move out of the objectified world, which has diminished our identity, silenced our voices in the face of the destruction of the natural world, and condoned costly patterns of domination of one human group over another.

Mysticism an Emerging Consciousness

The coincidence of the physicist's discovery and the mystic's knowing is a foundation for further evolution of consciousness. A number of people suggest that the early universe had from the beginning a latent form of consciousness. This is a fundamental consciousness that is distinguished from our ego consciousness of everyday life. As mentioned previously in connection with our new origin story, Whitehead thought that even elementary particles are endowed with some form or level of consciousness.[84] Brian Swimme teaches that consciousness was a dimension of the fireball in a latent sense; and that the universe had a psychic dimension from the beginning. It is described as a "biospiritual dimension in light and matter."[85] It is a kind of invisible latency waiting to emerge.

One reason for the marginal place of mysticism in Western culture, in addition to the dominance of mechanistic thought in science, may well be our failure to recognize its evolutionary significance. Congruent with the thought that the universe has a psychic/consciousness dimension from the beginning, it is proposed that mysticism is an emerging phenomenon. John Yungblut taught that everyone is a mystic, each with varying degrees of awareness. He wrote that "Mystical consciousness is that human faculty, new in evolutionary perspective, in which we can actually perceive the as-yet-unfinished creation still at work."[86] He believed it was the growing edge of humanity's continuing evolution. Physicists' discovery of the nonvisible interiority, the seamless plenum, can be an important impetus in the evolution of consciousness, help move mystical consciousness away from the margins, and encourage us to seek this higher (or deeper), more comprehensive consciousness.

The recognition of evolution by Charles Darwin and others in the 19th century, and the identification of past changes in human consciousness, such as, the first axial changes in consciousness occurring independently in several centers of civilization between 800 B.C.E. and 200 B.C.E., support the hope that ongoing change in human self-understanding and human consciousness can continue.[87] I have confidence there is an opening to further evolution of consciousness in the light of this coincidence of discovery by physicists and mystics.

This integration gives great added confidence to the depth of our participation in our creative, interconnected world. I have begun to dare hope that the integration described in these pages, as well as integrations by others previously cited, will become more available and understood. It is consciousness of the depth of our person and of the natural world. We can seek to be available to receive creative insights and participate in the evolution of our own self-understanding, in the evolution of human consciousness, and hopefully, along with others, the evolution of culture. We dare believe there can be a further emergence of consciousness, and perhaps some added wisdom. The contemporary widespread interest in a broad range of meditation practices and contemplative modes of living shared by many traditions east and west is strengthening the search for a deeply spiritual life, a deeply participatory life. The broad reach of the Internet enables significant teachings to become available in our living room. The mystics and contemplatives may have been a modest dimension of the religious world, but this may be fundamentally changing.

The contributions of the two disciplines, mysticism and quantum physics, are needed to heal the costly and dangerous western split, a split that is often internalized. I write in part as a witness to my too long delay in having confidence that I might participate in the hidden, numinous reality I had experienced so many years earlier. And I witness to the importance of this integration to heal that costly split that has meant that we have been unable to challenge the devaluing of too many people and the natural world.

The tree of life, a traditional image of the interconnectedness of life now has even greater spiritual significance given the discovery by physicists of the seamless plenum. I took the liberty of adding within the branches and roots the geometric,

Tree of Life – 1992

rectangular pattern with light shining inside the pattern. That shining light is intended to suggest the vast within, the seamless plenum, that physicists tell us is the mysterious reality in which the patterns of energy that form the manifest world, the tree and all the other beings, come into being. The unity of the tree of life image in the painting lies then not only in the visible, observed interconnections of the body of the tree itself, the living beings of the natural world like the toucan and the frog pictured within the branches but also in the unseen generative ground (the light inside the design) that permeates and sustains the diversified, interdependent visible world, moment by moment. The non-visible, seamless plenum is integral to the very atoms of Earth and hence all of its beings. The image was made into a poster with the title "Everything is Holy."[88]

Imaging and Naming of Sacred Presence

How do we name and talk about the mysterious reality that comprises our very being? The integration proposed in this chapter does not contradict nor invalidate many traditional images and conceptions of the sacred Presence. But it is also true that some old images can be seen to be misleading so they must be abandoned to allow for an evolution of our assumptions and understandings of the world and its sacred depth.

Can we use the word "God"? When people speak about God, I've noticed that they often point to the sky. Unfortunately, many people have become accustomed to images of God that do not assume the immanent presence of the sacred Presence in our daily world. Consequently, for these and other reasons, it will be wise to avoid that word "God" for a period while we are making the transition to the emerging worldview. We can, with care, use it again if our images are congruent with the transformed context of our evolutionary story and our radically new conceptions of matter. The images and practices of some eastern traditions are embraced by many people as they have found them congruent with their search for an integrated worldview. A long dialog engaging the discoveries of science and these traditions is before us.

In our new context of our evolutionary universe and earth, quantum physics, greater valuing of the countless testimonies of the mystical experiences, the influence of eastern traditions, many questions arise about naming and imaging the interiority of the manifest world. Since we are concerned with the unfolding cosmic story that integrates the nonvisible and manifest, we may ask if it is wise to name the interiority and thereby risk seeming to separate out the nonvisible, interior dimension from our daily physical world, our space-time world. It could seem to suggest a separation that is no longer possible, the same separation nondual traditions seek to avoid. However, many people are not aware of the nonvisible interiority of our daily world discovered by physicists so the naming is valuable as it serves to affirm the existence of the interior, numinous world and to instruct communities about this discovery and to explore the integration described in these pages.

If a person has begun their journey estranged from this depth of being, an initial awakening and naming is, according to Bede Griffiths, the Benedictine monk, an important stage. The naming of the dimension newly recognized by science, is important. Names are valuable as they help us talk about the nonvisible dimension of our identity and that of the natural world that has been widely lost. Names and images can invite questions and encourage us to ponder anew our identity. Perhaps years after an initial identification and naming, a person may move, Bede Griffiths suggested, toward a holistic, non-dual world.[89]

Use of words from science like "seamless plenum," as a way of naming the non-visible interiority of our world is a problem because such words will be heard to have very limited personal meaning. The language of science is arid and does not speak of the compelling felt experience the mystics describe and countless people have known. Working scientists are restrained from addressing publicly the personal significance of their discoveries and also from writing about how their discoveries may be experienced subjectively by an individual. A name from science may easily be quite limiting as the words and descriptions of the ultimate dimension of the finite must indicate its great personal and cultural significance as that reality is the foundation of our identity.

There are a number of words and phrases that may be valuable to name the nonvisible seamless interiority (seamless plenum) that both physicists and mystics are witnessing. We need to find words and images that speak to the heart yet are congruent with our profoundly changed worldview. These include: "Ground of Being," "sacred Presence," "creative Presence," "creative power," "all-nourishing abyss," "Light," "unseen Immensity," "Great Mystery," "Holy Mystery," "Source of all," "burning Oneness," "luminous web,"[90] and "pure Unmanifest."[91] Here are some additional valuable phrases: "numinous essence at the heart of existence,"[92] "the mystery at the base of things,"[93] the "unseen ocean of potentiality,"[94] "infinity of pure generative power,"[95] and the "realm of nonmaterial power."[96]

Belonging

This painting, "Belonging", celebrates a belonging in which the numinous energy that had awoken within me is integral to me and all of life that surrounds me. Although written in another context, the following words describe the profound belonging we are invited to embrace: "Now instead of being a cup going to the ocean and each time getting just a cup full, you are a cup living in the ocean being filled by the ocean itself ... the ocean of energy."[97]

In the pages that follow I will use the words "sacred Presence" as the name referring to the common insight derived from the seamless plenum and the "invisible fecundity" experienced by mystics. Although at times I will refer specifically to the seamless plenum when writing only in reference to the discovery of the nonvisible interiority by quantum physicists.

[handwritten margin note: author's name choices]

Belonging Within Our Unfolding Story

Confidence in the ongoing sacred Presence can be difficult to embrace as we live in an often violent and destructive world and we naturally ask if the sacred is within that violence and the suffering. The new story describes an unfolding whole so we cannot exclude violence and destruction as part of the whole. I immediately think of tragedies as my brother's death not being outside the sacred in this worldview. I am invited to think freshly about the suffering and to entertain new ways of embracing that tragedy. Those of us who did not experience a profound belonging because of personal family history, racism, extreme poverty and the western dualism of spirit and matter now clearly belong; we are given a sacred belonging. The intractable division between mind and soul in the Western tradition can heal and indeed must heal. As this integration is understood in the context of our evolutionary universe, fundamental possibilities of great significance become available. We seek ways to embrace and to celebrate this further awakening.

The origin story told by a culture molds the community's identity. There is reason to be hopeful that our most remarkable origin story will help transform human self-understanding, awakening us to the inestimable value of Earth and its inhabitants and increase our awareness of our common origins and common destiny. Instead of thinking of the universe as a background in which we exist, we realize we are an integral form, one among many, of the continually emerging totality.

CHAPTER FOUR
Becoming Fully Conscious Participants in the Unfolding Story

Embrace of Suffering

Thanks to my deepened understanding of human identity within our evolutionary story and the breakthrough in the recognition by physicists and mystics of the nonvisible sacred Presence integral to my very being, I dared to know with confidence that the loss of adequate nurture and the resulting suffering I experienced as an infant, described in the first chapter, are not the final word. The situation of the person who suffers is profoundly different within our new context as compared to a dualistic world that separates our bodies and the natural world from spirit (*prana or ruah*). In the dualistic world we do not know that the spirit, the dynamic and life-giving energy of the universe, is intrinsic to our very being, always present and active. In our new worldview there is an identity not circumscribed by the loss and suffering; the ongoing sacred Presence (seamless plenum) provides a place to stand, a willingness to feel the suffering deeply with confidence in the possibility of fresh emergence, a fresh expression of the Self. We can be confident that we can become true differentiated subjects in communion with our world and other people, given the ancient archetypal patterning intrinsic to the person.

Of fundamental importance to me was learning and trusting that the sacred Presence remained integral to my being even though it was not fully drawn forth and experienced in relationships of love and attention in those early years. The tragedy made my full identity obscure and hidden given the defenses that developed. So in the context of our profound belonging in our new understanding of the nature of the manifest world and the formation of the Self within it, I found important

56

encouragement to search for and embrace the fullness and wholeness of my being in the midst of the suffering. I had not been completely abandoned as I was always integral to the sacred Presence and the patterns of energy arising within it. We have discovered a profound belonging in which one dares to engage with the suffering. We can be confident that a greater realized fullness may emerge even though it was not fully nurtured into consciousness in childhood. We can come home as we are integral to the unfolding whole.

The Self May Be Recovered

While the Self may not be fully embodied and expressed in the psychological and physical development of the child and growing person, the archetypal pattern, the Self, a near equivalent of soul, does not disappear as it is part of the fundamental ordering that is a pattern intrinsic to the person developed in evolutionary history. Ervin Laszlo writes that the inner ordering may be viewed as a kind of intelligence, a general sort of "psyche" operating in the womb of nature.[98] Lionel Corbet describes archetypes as *a priori* patterns, laws of consciousness.[99] This is the gift of subjectivity, which is another way of saying that everyone as a human being has a profound depth of belonging, wounded or whole. The Self/soul may be brought forth in later years; wounding is not the final story.

Walter Brueggemann's book *The Prophetic Imagination*, is based on his study of the writings of the prophet Jeremiah. Brueggemann argues that the leaders of the Israelites in exile in Babylonia were unable to face their tragic historical situation because of their numbed consciousness. The only way to penetrate the numbed consciousness of denial he argues was by public expression of grief. Articulated grief, he writes, is the gate of newness.[100] Newness comes precisely from expressed pain. Brueggeman writes: "There is grief work to be done in the present that the future may come."[101] In the context of my emerging confidence in the remarkable depth of the human person, I could hear what Walter Brueggemann was saying and understand the fundamental role of grief and suffering in personal and cultural change.

I had not previously understood that embrace of suffering is often required in the pathway to some recovery of fullness of being. As described in earlier pages I had become aware of some of my unconscious patterns which defended me against suffering but this awareness is not the same as felt grief. A man in our group studying Brueggemann told us that before he was born, his family lost a four-year-old child in complex and tragic circumstances. This tragedy profoundly affected his entire family including his father with whom he was closely connected. Consequently, his family, like mine, did not provide a home in which he was loved and embraced as a unique, special child. Early experiences of the sacred that had meant so much to him when he was a young boy wandering in a nearby woods, stopped occurring as he coped with the family situation.

There are difficult periods in the journey to wholeness. Beverly Lanzetta, a sister student at Fordham University writes in *The Path of the Heart*: "One must be in darkness to see and in silence to hear.[102] "To find things in the dark one must look in the darkness. It is through, and not in spite of, our inner wounds that we taste the goodness and all-encompassing love of God.[103] I delayed far too long addressing my inner wounding and my unconscious defenses. For many years I had not learned a "way of seeing" that offered a home, a belonging that I could trust and dare experience the partly buried suffering. The changes in worldview explored in previous pages brought knowledge of my belonging that gave me the confidence to embrace the consequences of my early experience. There can be a reweaving of the mortal heart, Beverly Lanzatta wrote, into the fabric of God's self.

It moves me to tears that my mother's suffering and my suffering are not the end of the story. The suffering, however costly, does contain the pathway to meaning and wholeness if the grief becomes consciously felt. Acknowledgement of suffering meant a freedom to dare to be more aware of the psychological patterns that had protected me to some degree from suffering. A number of times I thought that if I had a choice, I would not choose to be born again under the tragic circumstances and deep suffering into which I was born. Many people born in very difficult circumstances must think the same thing; too many people resort to suicide, to drugs and alcohol. Such tragic roads may be avoided if the fullness of our identity that we are now understanding could be recognized and embraced more widely. Remarkably it is the very felt suffering in which the profound belonging my mother could not offer is to be found as my mother's suffering was also integral to the sacred Presence.

The felt suffering is a profound belonging. Sacred Presence was not absent from me and my mother in the midst of the suffering; we realize with our new holistic understanding that it is never absent. There is a home in which the great passivities that Teilhard de Chardin wrote about can be addressed and possibly resolved. Many people in the past have had faith that this is so.

The center of identity can be recovered when the suffering is no longer denied and repressed. This difficult pathway is one that must be embraced again and again, now profoundly supported in the context of our new origin story and new discoveries about the interiority of matter and many insights in psychology. We enter into a growing confidence and greater openness to knowing we are embedded within a healing, creative reality, a reality with numinous depths.

Recall the earlier discussions about self-organizing, a deep inner ordering, that is soul-like in the person. It does not arise from conscious effort, although conscious cooperation plays a role in its expression. It means a great deal to the wounded person that we are ordered by the dynamics of the universe, not by ego efforts nor only by our defenses that protected us from further wounding. New ordering and recovery of inner order that was hidden by defenses, appear especially in times of chaos, both personal and collective. In these times of political, social, and ecological crises, confidence in the possibility of recovered and new order is particularly important.

According to Anthony Stevens, a Jungian analyst who writes about evolutionary psychiatry, healing is "a question of channeling powerful propensities that are as old as evolution itself."[104] The powerful potentialities are the ordering patterns, the archetypal endowment, that guides and controls the life cycle of the human species and the common cultural patterns. These include rules governing courtship, marriage, adultery, funeral rites, mental illness, and laws about property, among others. These propensities or predispositions are the end products of a process of natural selection peculiar to the human species.[105]

Edward Edinger, a Jungian analyst and author, calls the recovery of fundamental identity "the recovery of the ego-Self axis".[106] Jung saw the Self as the psychological manifestation of Deity. This insight by Jung gives support to the worldview developed in these pages. Awakening experiences would be occasions of the beginning of recovery of the Self and the emergence of conscious connections of the Self with the ego. This can also be described as the recovery of soul, the near equivalent of the self, and the capacity of the soul to know or experience and live within the sacred Presence. Nurturing relationship can enable this recovery of the Self. Clearly conscious experience of suffering is an occasion of recovery of the ego-Self axis, as the defenses against the suffering that have blocked felt awareness of the depth of being have weakened.

I have come to see that the place of connectedness with my mother was in the suffering itself. That is where she was living. I regret that we never were able to carefully talk and cry together about our shared suffering. A different, deeper relationship would have emerged had we been able to grieve together. It would have been within an encompassing mother-child relationship that can carry the sacred Presence. It took decades for me to address the suffering. Unless the suffering is deeply, consciously experienced, there is a protective restriction and narrowing of felt knowledge of our shared belonging rooted in the pervasive sacred Presence. Suffering is one of the openings to love.

Tragedy and suffering carry a certain destiny as they do compel one to face the wounding and search to recover the hidden depth of being that did not find a full awakening within childhood. There is a compelling urgency to find healing as we are attracted by the beauty and felt great value of spiritual experience and the hope of loving relationships and communities. I have come to understand that my wounding, though costly, did compel a search for healing, understanding, and a pathway within our contemporary world, which now includes the breakthroughs in physics! Although I describe this in a relatively academic manner, it has been a long, engaging spiritual journey over decades of therapy, study, and retreats.

Dark Night of the Culture

Bede Griffiths, the Benedictine monk, observed that we are within a dark night as a culture. Unfortunately, the list of crises, including nuclear weaponry, climate disruption, overpopulation and ongoing war, threaten the integrated life systems of Earth and human viability within them. Our fractured culture and our destruction of the natural world is bringing a severe dislocation. Our slow response to these crises gives rise to fundamental questions.

Thomas Berry writes that our collective behavior represents a crisis of commitment to life itself. The solution to the crisis of commitment is to recover our deeper self, to evoke once again those psychic energies that have dwindled in recent centuries. Part of the pathway for the individual is the encounter with grief. We may be acquainted with grief in our individual lives, but as a society we have yet to grieve for the rivers that no longer flow and forests that are gone forever. The same wounding that prevents our individual fulfillment can block a felt response to the environmental crisis.

It is very difficult in our culture for us to grieve these losses as the natural world has been objectified and commodified, discouraging our felt love and deep belonging within our home. There is hope that as we enter our new evolutionary story and grasp the depth of our origins within it and our deep belonging integral to Earth, we will grieve for Earth and its beings and be moved to a transformed relationship with Earth.

Despair and Empowerment

In her book *Despair and Personal Power in the Nuclear Age,*[107] Joanna Macy offers a process called "Despair and Empowerment" to help free us from the consequences of repressed feelings by which we hide and avoid the fears evoked by the pain of the world and the threats to our future. The despair and empowerment work seeks to help us unblock our numbed energies to release our vitality and our power to act. She quotes Dorothee Sölle who wrote "Suffering is a form of change that a person experiences; it is a mode of becoming."[108] Our public apathy is "but a fear of experiencing and expressing this pain, and that once it is acknowledged and shared it opens the way to our power."[109] First developed in her work on the threat of nuclear war, it can also, of course, free energy to address our repressed feelings about the degradation and destruction of the natural world. She writes that we lead a double life, focusing on business as usual while our repressed feelings undermine the sources of creativity.[110] We can become available to higher consciousness. Until we do, our power of creative response will be crippled.

Teilhard de Chardin was concerned with awakening the power of human communities to address the major crises facing humanity. While serving as a stretcher bearer in World War I he experienced a powerful bonding with his companions in the trenches; it was a time of untold shared suffering. From this experience he knew humanity's capacity to coalesce in groupings that belong to a higher order, an order of love.[111] He called the envelope of human consciousness that is emerging as part of evolution, the "noosphere", a term he coined. It is the spiritual milieu in which each human is intimately connected with all of humanity.[112] He was confident that when individuals unite, they become capable of more being. There is a creative union that enhances the individual; it is not a collectivization that diminishes the individual's creative role. It certainly involves preparation that deepens our participation, like the preparation for the individual.

Quakers have had a similar realization. They seek as a group in silence to discern whether to undertake a particular action or find another direction when faced with an important decision. Out of the silence individuals in the group may occasionally speak as led to contribute to the discernment process. It is understood that a community can arrive at a decision or an understanding that would not have been possible for an individual alone. This process is done in a worshipful manner, seeking inner guidance.

In the face of the prospect of a worsening of the already difficult life for many people as the sustaining capacity of Earth is degraded, we may ask if enough people have the psychic energy and even the basis of hope to address the many pressing issues before us. If people are depressed and hopeless a functioning, life-giving story is essential. I have confidence that the worldview explored in these pages is part of the awakening we all long for. As the story is internalized, there can be a collective awakening. Humanity can bond at ever deeper levels. The emerging worldview promises a great energy available within us and around us if we learn to embrace our identity within the unfolding story. Teilhard de Chardin wrote: "The internal face of the world comes to light and reflects upon itself in the very depths of our human consciousness."[113]

Finding Wisdom is State Dependent

The seamless plenum integrated with insights from mystics and the evolutionary story provide pathways to healing, one of which is to engage with suffering. This offers us an identity within which to ponder past insights into wisdom and to have confidence that people in the future will learn to live wisely.

Cynthia Bourgeault, Episcopal priest, retreat leader and author, teaches that the Wisdom tradition is "a precise and comprehensive science of spiritual transformation that has existed since the headwaters of the great world religions and is in fact their common ground."[114] She describes how the Wisdom tradition teaches people to find patterns of work and prayer based on the understanding that finding Wisdom is state dependent. The wisdom tradition works with the whole person and the individual's whole pattern of life.

Ervin Laszlo writes in a similar vein that a coherent brain and body receives and transmits the intelligence of the cosmos with more articulation and greater detail than a less coherent brain and body. He writes that an evolved consciousness provides guidance for the brain and body in achieving internal wholeness, harmony with the external world.[115] He also points out a depth level of consciousness may emerge into prominence when the everyday operations of the brain are slowed or shut down. Meditation can prepare space for wisdom and higher consciousness to emerge. We may find our way to a condition of the person where, as Bevelry Lanzetta wrote, purpose and meaning can be experienced, not thought and postulated.[116]

The pathway to wisdom values the three central governing tendencies of evolution, one of which is subjectivity. Thomas Berry writes that "Every being has its own divine numinous subjectivity, its self, its center, its unique reality.[117] "The recognition that the universe makes centers of subjectivity means that we are unique persons with a numinous center. This is based on the self-organizing that grounds subjectivity in the non-visible realm. It is most heartening that with this understanding of subjectivity each person is enabled, as Thomas Berry writes, to resonate with that numinous mystery that pervades the world. Over time, increased subjectivity is associated with increased complexity of the nervous system including development of the brain. With a more complex nervous system, individuals become more self-determining with multiple modes of expression.

The governing principle of differentiation means that as forms are generated within the unfolding whole, life on planet earth finds expression in an overwhelming variety of beings, including human beings. Each form (being) remains simultaneously part of the whole, yet also a unique being. Each articulation, Berry writes, is unrepeatable and irreplaceable. This fundamental differentiation, together with subjectivity, means that our identity need not be earned by achievement as individuality is a gift of the universe. It invites a fundamental self-acceptance of a unique identity. Unique individuality is not destroyed by adversity. The wounding does not erase this fundamental individuality although too often it may not be fully embraced and expressed. This is a more fundamental individuality than that of the ego, although the ego may aid in its expression or it may also obscure its expression.

As the universe differentiates into unique, particular beings who are subjects, it does not cease at the same time being in communion. Communion means that each person or a bird is differentiated within the unfolding whole, such that each being remains part of the whole. This communion is fundamental. Brian Swimme writes: "All that exists shapes the same energy that erupted into the universe at the primal fireball or big bang."[118]

The seamless plenum is a basis of communion as well as the other two governing principles. Ervin Laszlo writes of a whole, non-local consciousness field which would be a fundamental dimension of communion.[119] Fritjof Capra, an Austrian-born American physicist and systems theorist, writes in *Belonging to the Universe* "ultimately, there are no parts at all. What we call a part is merely a pattern in an inseparable world of relationships."[120] An email brought these words written by Dr. Martin Luther King about communion: "We are caught in an inescapable network of mutuality tied into a single garment of destiny. We are made to live together because of the interrelated structure of reality. It all boils down to this: that all life is interrelated."[121]

God Cannot Resist a Prepared Soul

It is heartening that Teresa of Avila, the 16th century Spanish mystic and reformer of the Carmelite order and doctor of the Roman Catholic Church, tells us that a certain priest taught her God is always present and that her experience confirmed this. She taught that with preparation this Presence will be known, because as she puts it "God cannot resist a prepared soul." Her teaching, although within a somewhat different worldview, offers the same most hopeful and important insight comparable to that of Laszlo and Bourgeault when they write that wisdom is state dependent; Teresa also taught us to prepare, to find our way into a condition, a state of being, which "God cannot resist."

Writing about the spiritual journey, Louis Dupré observed that "following the years of gradual change, the real is no longer an object that reason places before the mind, but rather a totality of which the mind constitutes an integral dynamic part."[122] Within the integration developed in the previous chapter, a person may find the confidence to search to be prepared and to find a way to an integral belonging within the sacred Presence and the patterns of energy of our very being and all of life.

An Image of Integral Belonging

Teresa of Avila's teaching that God "cannot resist a prepared soul" was written in the context of her remarkable image of the person living within a castle made of diamond or a very clear crystal. It is an image congruent with our discovery of the nonvisible interiority of the person as the castle itself is made of diamond, which we can understand as the nonvisible and as an image of the patterns of energy, sometimes experienced as light. In her earlier writings, the castle image, thought to come from Islamic sources, was made of gold and precious stones. She changed the image based on her experience and used it in her book, *The Interior Castle*. She changed the image to a castle made of diamond based on her vision that the Divinity is like a very clear diamond, much greater than all the world. She writes: "We could say that everything we do is visible in this diamond since it is of such a kind that it contains all things within itself; there is nothing that escapes its magnitude."[123] The interior castle made of very clear diamond is an image of that experience of all-pervasive Presence that she has known both inner to herself and around her. I personally cannot help but see the contemporary discovery of the seamless plenum in her image. It is an image congruent with the integration described in the previous chapter. The clear, transparent nature of the diamond is comparable to the nonvisible interiority of matter, the seamless plenum. The image of a castle made of diamond can well be an image of the nature of the nonvisible dimension of the reality we dwell within and is within us. I find the coincidence of insight remarkable and heartening! The image of the interior castle gains renewed life and truthfulness in our contemporary new context. She tells us in her last book, *The Interior Castle*, that as a consequence of the change in her understanding of her identity based on her experience, she was compelled to live congruent with her experience, although as she writes herself, subject to error.

A Long Journey of Preparation

According to legend, Parsifal, an orphaned young man, wandered into the land of the grail castle. As he walked into that sacred land, he killed a swan which, as depicted in one staging of the opera, he was proudly dragging by the neck as he approached the castle. He had killed it not knowing that animals were protected in that sacred land. Although he watched the religious services of the brothers of the Holy Grail and spoke with Gunemanz, a brother who hoped he was the leader they had been promised by tradition, Parsifal departed not knowing the special significance of the place and the community he had come upon. It took many years of wandering and trials before he returned to join and lead the brotherhood. I fear that similarly too many of us do not know fully the beauty and great value of the particular place and community and bioregion where we live. So we wander for too many years. The insights brought by the new evolutionary origin story and the new physics can lead us to know the beauty of the land and all its beings so, like Parsifal, we will learn to see with new eyes and an engaged heart. We learn we are already in the land of the grail castle. The sacred beauty will no longer be hidden so we are moved to protect the swans, the humans and other beings of land and sea and air.

Creativity Emerges within a Deep Belonging

The evolutionary story tells us there is a possibility of a new emergence we haven't previously imagined. Creation is not simply an event in the past. Brian Swimme wrote in *The Hidden*

Heart of the Cosmos "That which gave birth to the universe is giving birth in this moment as well. ... We are led inexorably to reflect upon the thrilling and unnerving fact that the power that gave birth to the universe suffuses our flesh and blood."[124] With integration within the source, the sacred Presence, it is possible a pathway to the creation of a viable future may slowly emerge. This is heartening, given the fundamental need for an evolution of human consciousness. With preparation, individuals and groups can learn to enter into the sacred Presence so we find hope in the possibility of creative emergence. We can seek to be available to receive creative insights. The person has a greater agency and more choices, bringing hope that with wisdom, a viable future may emerge. There is no full understanding, but the discoveries require our attention as they are world-changing for us all. Hallelujah!

Philip Clayton, Arthus Peacocke, and others are studying and writing about emergent processes within panentheism, a tradition that has long sought to embrace the thrust of modern

Ongoing Creativity

A small, crocheted piece and some quilted designs are collaged on a watercolor to celebrate the creativity of women over the centuries. Their work is included with the images of Earth and a galaxy, places of great creativity.

science in its thought.[125] With this integration the creative work of people and groups can be included within the unfolding story in which the sacred presence is integral to the whole. This is important because it adds creativity as a fundamental category in philosophy and religion.

Thomas Berry teaches that any creative deed at the human level is a continuation of the creativity of the universe.[126] The new spirituality invites creative participation in the earth community as Earth is coming into being and we are part of it. Although we might fear for the human future, our preparation holds great promise as it is supported by the profound change in cosmology.

The sacred Presence is not readily experienced by the individual nor is it readily expressed in western culture. According to Louis Dupré, there is an initially given unity of the soul with God, using his language, although it is only potentially expressed in daily life by the actual living person by growth in love and a journey of transformation.[127] The integration of the seamless plenum and mystical testimony we are exploring affirms this initially given unity although with some changed assumptions within the new cosmology. Most often it is only thru a long transformative journey that expression of it becomes possible in a person's daily life. We have a capacity for consciousness of this identity as the mystics have told us. Countless traditions, teachers, books and living witnesses offer guidance on the topic of being prepared.

I find spiritual practices taught in the context of our evolutionary universe enlightening and encouraging. Craig Hamilton teaches meditation in the field of evolutionary spirituality. He was senior editor of the magazine "What Is Enlightenment?" and founder of Integral Enlightenment that teaches on-line meditation classes. He teaches, congruent with the integration proposed in this book, ways to become conscious of the infinite sacred depth integral to our being. Hamilton teaches meditations designed to enable the meditator to become aware of this identity, which he refers to as the awareness in which thoughts and feeling are arising. He teaches that even though emotional and psychological pain are part of the moment, when we meditate, they need not prevent us from being fully present as we are taught not to engage with those feelings.[128] Despite pain we can still awaken to the divine mystery that is always present. If we are still, relaxed and paying attention, an awareness of our identity may arise.

There is an oft repeated topic of discussion which is whether there is a sound when a tree falls in the woods if there is no one in the woods to hear it. Most commonly it is argued that of course there is a sound since the tree did fall causing the vibrations in the air. Actually, if there is no person with an ear (nor other beings with ears or ways of being sensitive to air waves) that responds to the vibrating air and no brain interpreting the vibrations in the ear drum, there is no sound. There is only the vibration of the air caused by the falling tree which will gradually dissipate. It is remarkable that without the person to bring forth a quality of the vibrating air, its potential to be sound, that possibility does not come into being. The sound simply is not brought into being without the person with ears, an interpreting brain and a listening heart. Doesn't this role of the human ear and brain in relation to the air waves clarify the nature of our role in our emergent universe? We must be prepared to receive the creative impulses.

There was an article about Sri Aurobindo in the magazine *What Is Enlightenment?* by Craig Hamilton that indicates further the hope in the spiritual journey in the context of evolution. "Once the soul, or psychic being, comes forward or emerges in the individual, there is a natural dynamic aspiration that overrides all of the resistances of the ego and lower nature. It's like the ego gets kicked out of the driver's seat and God takes over the wheel, as you."[129] Then the path can unfold organically. That is deep participation with the evolution of the universe.

With awareness that our lives are integral to the creative whole, we realize that we may play a crucial role in the emergence of ideas and actions. Furthermore, we see clearly that the seamless plenum which from the perspective of science may have seemed cold and impersonal, becomes a lived reality.

Jesus of Nazareth

The affirmation of our radical spiritual identity as described in these pages, is not new to the Christian tradition, given its statements that God (the sacred Presence) was incarnate (within the flesh) of Jesus of Nazareth. According the Louis Dupré, the affirmation that, in a most intimate way, the Christian is united with God is the core of mystical theology, an undeniable essence of Christian faith.[130] Jesus was a revelation of the fullness of human identity lived among us in daily life. His life has awakened countless people to the fullness of human possibility.

In the book *Reimagining God and Religion*, the Jungian analyst and former Presbyterian minister Jerry Wright identifies a number of remarkable people who came to know experientially the immanent numinous dimension of the human being and the natural world. Wright understands that the awakening of numinous experiences are revelations of the Self, the central soul-like characteristic of the person that is identified by the sacred Presence. The soul has the capacity to unite to the ground of being. When there is such a union, the person may become Christ-like. Wright objects to the use of the word "Christ" to refer to Jesus of Nazareth alone, obscuring the knowledge that many people come to realize a full, differentiated expression of the Self and thus become Christs. John Yungblut reflected a similar understanding when he decried the profound diminishment of indwelling divine when it is attributed to Jesus alone.[131] Wright names other religious figures who reveal the Self/Christ: Buddha, Purusha, Tao, Khidr, and Tifereth.[132] The integration proposed in these pages is a source of increased confidence that we too may seek to enter a fuller expression of our identity.

It is not easy for Western people to embrace the break-throughs in our understanding of human identity and the nature of the natural world now available to us from the integration proposed in these pages and knowledge from many great figures. But it may well be a gift to us as a threatened species because it can strengthen the witness of many people, as exemplified by Jesus of Nazareth, and broaden the scope of our witness. This fullness may be expressed by many people in different modes of being as courageous witnesses for the well-being of Earth. A more inclusive truth struggles to be born.

Allurement

In Brian Swimme's video series *Powers of the Universe*, allurement is one of the ten powers of the universe that he identifies based on the perspective offered by our knowledge of the history of the universe. One way the universe works in human beings is by alluring us and by captivating us. People are allured to search for truth, to find love; people are allured by music, by sports, by sailing, by painting, by beauty, by the search for justice and by a countless number of important ways of living. I was allured by the promise of the depth of our belonging in the new story. It is a very attractive invitation to release ourselves into the field of allurement and trust its unfolding in conscious self-awareness. That awakening experience in the bedroom long ago was profoundly alluring. In the understanding of process theology, the drive to discover truth or to advocate for truth is divinely instilled. I am most grateful to the allurement of the emerging new story as I have largely found my way out of the suffering caused by the crippling effects on my mother when her young son, my brother, died. I hope this account of my journey and the various discoveries and insights from science and the contemplative tradition, will allure the reader and offer hope to those who have also faced difficult life-defining passivities.

Garden Profusion

I end with two paintings that celebrate the allure of the new story and the allure of beauty. On the previous page is "Garden Profusion".

The painting "New Tiffany Windows" below is a witness to the hope that, in the light of our new discoveries, we can regain felt knowledge of the sacred Presence throughout the natural world so the world may be resacralized. The Tiffany panels on either side of the painting would traditionally frame scenes from the life of Jesus of Nazareth. Now their framing could also be used to celebrate our recognition of the sacred Presence in the natural world in the light of the discoveries of the seamless plenum and the testimony of the mystics.

New Tiffany Window

Sr. Miriam MacGillis, founder of Genesis Farm, has suggested that the foundations for a new culture are being laid. We are offered a radical identity in which personal and cultural change may come into being. May we as individuals and as communities have the courage to reimagine our identity within the unfinished journey of Earth and cosmos.

Endnotes

1) Tart, 2009. Chapter 20.

2) Richard Tarnas, 2007.

3) Louis Dupré, 1976, p. 93.

4) Teresa of Avila, 1987, pp. 109-125, Mary Coelho, 1987.

5) Teresa of Avila, 1976, 28.9,

6) Teilhard de Chardin, 1957, p. 75.

7) Brian Swimme, 1990. *Feast of Consciousness. Canticle to the Cosmos.* Center for the Story of the Universe, DVD <storyoftheuniverse.org/store>.

8) Brian Swimme, 2004. *Seamlessness. Powers of the Universe*, Center for the Story of the Universe, DVD <storyoftheuniverse.org/store/>.

9) Brian Swimme 2019, pp. 108, 109.

10) Mary Evelyn Tucker and John Grimm, 2009, p. 25.

11) Thomas Berry, 1999, p. 49.

12) Mary Evelyn Tucker, John Grim, Andrew Augyal, 2019, p. 118.

13) Brian Swimme, 1984, p. 40.

14) Sam Mackintosh, 2019, 39.

15) Brian Swimme, 1990. *Feast of Consciousness. Canticle to the Cosmos.* Center for the Story of the Universe, DVD <storyoftheuniverse.org/store>.

16) Sam Mackintosh, 2019, p.39

17) Thomas Berry and Mary Evelyn Tucker, 2009, p. 75.

18) John Polkinghorne, 1998, p. 61.

19) Brian Swimme & Thomas Berry, 1992, p. 75.

20) F. David Peat, 1987, p. 88.

21) Brian Swimme, 2019, p. 104.

22) Thomas Berry and Mary Evelyn Tucker, 2006, p. 117.

23) Michael Comforti, 1999, p. xiii.

24) Brian Swimme and Thomas Berry, 1992, p. 71,72.

25) Bede Griffiths, 1989, p. 28.

26) Thomas Berry, 1999, p. 32.

27) Brian Swimme, 1984, p. 40.

28) John F. Haught, 2017, p.73.

29) Sam Mackintosh, 2019, p. 56.

30) Carlo Rovelli, 2014, pp. 54-62.

31) Carlo Rovelli, 2014, p. 55.

32) Carlo Rovelli, 2014, p. 56.

33) Carlo Rovelli, 2014, p. 59.

34) Fritjof Capra, 1975, p. 47.

35) Brian Swimme, 2019, p. 109.

36) Brian Swimme, 2019, p. 100.

37) Carlo Rovelli, 2014, p. 108

38) Carlo Rovelli, 2014, p. 108.

39) Brian Swimme, 2019, p. 108.

40) Brian Swimme, 2019, p. 108.

41) Brian Swimme, 2019, p. 109.

42) Brian Swimme, 2019, p. 100.

43) Brian Swimme, 2019, p. 100.

44) Fred Alan Wolf, 1999, p. 127.

45) Sarbmeet Kanwal, physicist, in the course Cosmos, Consciousness and Birthing the Ecozoic on the Deeptime Journey Network, October, 2020.

46) Brian Swimme, 2019, p. 109.

47) David Bohm, 1983, p.191.

48) K.C. Cole, 2001, p. 69.

49) Carlo Rovelli, 2014.

50) Brian Swimme, 1989, p. 80.

51) Brian Swimme & Thomas Berry, 1992. p. 17.

52) Brian Swimme, *Seamlessness. Powers of the Universe*, Center for the Story of the Universe, DVD <storyoftheuniverse.org/store/>.

53) Lothar Schafer, 1997, p.5

54) Brian Swimme and Thomas Berry, 1992, p. 28.

55) Brian Swimme and Thomas Berry, 1992, p. 28.

56) Herman Greene, 2018, p. 21.

57) Louis Dupré, 1989, p.7.

58) Louis Dupré, 1989, p.7.

59) Thomas Merton, 1963.

60) C. G. Jung, as quoted in Jerry R. Wright, 2018, p. 184.

61) Louis Dupré, 1989, p. 16.

62) Rumi as quoted in in the course Cosmos, Consciousness and Birthing the Ecozoic on the Deeptime Journey Network, October, 2020.

63) Pierre Teilhard de Chardin, 1978, p. 16.

64) Newell, 2008, p. 68.

65) John Yungblut, 1983, p. 17.

Endnotes

66) Catherine of Genoa, Vita e Dottrina, cap xiv.

67) Jan van Ruusbroec, Spiritual Espousals, Preface, p. xiii.

68) Raymond Bernard Blakney, 1941, p. 205.

69) Hafiz – in the dedication in a book of Hafiz'poems.

70) Brian Swimme, 2019, p. 105.

71) Pierre Teilhard de Chardin, 1978, p. 15.

72) Pierre Teilhard de Chardin, 1978, p. 24.

73) Pierre Teilhard de Chardin, 1978, p. 26.

74) Edward C Whitmont, 1993, p. 43.

75) Fritjof Capra, 1975, p. 5.

76) John Hagelin (interview), 2004 <edgemagazine.net/2004/01/hagelin>.

77) Ervin Laszlo, 2006, p. 2.

78) Laszlo, 2006, p. 25.

79) Laszlo, 2006, p. 27.

80) Pierre Teilhard de Chardin, 1959. p. 30.

81) Philip Clayton, 2004, p. 85.

82) Louis Dupré, 1989, p. 21.

83) Jalal al-Din Rumi <poets.org/poet/jalal-al-din-rumi>.

84) Laszlo, 2006, p. 53.

85) Brian Swimme, 1990. *Feast of Consciousness. Canticle to the Cosmos.* Center for the Story of the Universe, DVD <storyoftheuniverse.org/store>.

86) John Yungblut, 1979, p. 45.

87) Karl Jaspers, 1953.

88) In gratitude to Ruah Swennerfelt and Quaker Earthcare Witness for making the poster.

89) Bede Griffiths, 1989.

90) Cynthia Bourgeault, 2003, p. 46.

91) Cynthia Bourgeault, 2003, p. 45.

92) Jerry R. Wright, 2018, p. 34.

93) Brian Swimme, 2019, p. 100.

94) Ibid, p. 100.

95) Ibid, p. 100.

96) Ibid, p. 98.

97) Andrew Harvey, 2001, p. 61.

98) Erwin Laszlo, 1998, pp. 220, 221.

99) Lionel Corbet, 1996, p. 58.

100) Walter Brueggemann, 2001, pp 81, 91, 92.

101) Ibid, p. 119.

102) Beverly Lanzetta, 1985, p. 62.

103) Higgins and Burns, 2012.

104) Anthony Stevens, 1993, p. 98.

105) Ibid, pp. 15-19.

106) Edward Edinger, 1972, pp. 56-61.

107) Joanna Rogers Macy,1983, pp. 1-19.

108) Ibid, 1983, p. 19.

109) Ibid, 1983, p. 19.

110) Ibid, 1983. p. 13.

111) Pierre Teilhard de Chardin, 1978, p. 30.

112) Kathleen Duffy, SSJ, 2019, p. 39.

113) Pierre Teilhard de Chardin, 1959, p. 29.

114) Cynthia Bourgeault, 2003, pp. xvi, xvii.

115) Ervin Laszlo, 2017, p. 46.

116) Beverly Lanzetta, 1985, p. 15.

117) Thomas Berry and Mary Evelyn Tucker, 2009, p. 78.

118) Brian Swimme, 1990.

119) Ervin Laszlo, 2017, p. 60.

120) Fritjof Capra and David Steindl-Rast, 1991, p. xii

121) Martin Luther King, Jr., 1967. A Christmas Sermon on Peace. <youtube. com/watch?v=1jeylAH3bUl>.

122) Louis Dupré, 1989, p. 21.

123) Teresa of Avila, 1976, 40.10.

124) Brian Swimme, 2019, p. 112.

125) Philip Clayton, 2004, pp. 84-91.

126) Thomas Berry and Mary Evelyn Tucker, 2006. p. 59.

127) Louis Dupré, 1989, p. 17.

128) Craig Hamilton, March 21, 2019 "This Is It" <Integral Enlightenment.com>.

129) Craig Hamilton, "Why Sri Aurobindo Is Cool" ISSU <issuu.com/crisrich/ docs/why_sri_aurobindo_is_cool>.

130) Louis Dupré, 1989, p. 5.

131) Charles C. Finn, 2012, p. 12.

132) Jerry R. Wright, 2018. p. 112.

Bibliography

Thomas Berry, 2000. *The Great Work: Our Way Into the Future.* New York, NY: Bell Tower.

Thomas Berry and Mary Evelyn Tucker. 2006. *Evening Thoughts: Reflecting on Earth as Sacred Community,* San Francisco: Sierra Club Books.

Thomas Berry and Mary Evelyn Tucker, 2009. *The Sacred Universe: Earth, Spirituality, and Religion in the Twenty-First Century.* New York NY: Columbia University Press.

Raymond Bernard Blakney, 1941. *Meister Eckhart, A Modern Translation.* New York: Harper & Brothers.

David Bohm, 1983. *Wholeness and the Implicate Order* (London and New York: Ark PaperbPauliacks.

Cynthia Bourgeault, 2003. *The Wisdom Way of Knowing.* San Francisco, CA: John Wiley and Sons.

Walter Brueggemann, 2001. *The Prophetic Imagination.* Minneapolis: Fortress Press.

Fritjof Capra, 1975. *The Tao of Physics.* Boulder, Colorado: Shambala Publications.

Fritjof Capra and David Steindl-Rast, 1991. *Belonging to the Universe.* San Francisco: Harper Collins.

Catherine of Genoa. *Vita e Dottrina,* cap xiv.

Pierre Teilhard de Chardin, 1957. *The Divine Milieu.* New York NY: Harper and Row.

Pierre Teilhard de Chardin, 1959. *The Phenomenon of Man.* New York: Harper and Row.

Pierre Teilhard de Chardin, 1978. *The Heart of Matter.* Translated by René Hague. New York: Harcourt Brace Jovanovich.

Philip Clayton, 2004. "Panentheism in Metaphysical and Scientific Perspective" In *Whom We Live and Move and Have Our Being,* ed. Philip Clayton and Arthur Peacocke. Grand Rapids, Michigan: William B Eerdmans Publishing Company.

Mary C. Coelho, 1987. St. Teresa of Avila's Transformation of the Symbol of the Interior Castle. Teresianum 38: 109-125.

Michael Comforti, 1999. *Field, Form and Fate.* Woodstock, CT: Spring Publications Inc.

Lionel Corbet, 1996. *The Religious Function of the Psyche.* New York, NY: Routledge.

K.C. Cole, 2001. *A Hole in the Universe.* New York: Harcourt.

Kathleen Duffy, SSJ, 2019. *Teilhard's Struggle.* Maryknoll, New York: Orbis Books.

Louis Dupré, 1976. *Transcendent Selfhood.* New York NY: Seabury Press.

Louis Dupré, 1989. "Unio mystica: The State and the Experience," in *Mystical Union and Monotheistic Faith: An Ecumenical Dialogue,* ed. Moshe Idel and Bernard McGinn. New York: Macmillan.

Edward Edinger, 1972. *Ego and Archetype,* New York: G. P. Putnam's Sons.

Charles C. Finn, 2012. *John Yungblut, Passing the Mystical Torch.* Wallingford, PA: Pendle Hill Publications #417.

Herman Greene, 2018. *The Long View: Thomas Berry's Instruction on the Reform of Religion, Law, and Culture in His Later Books.* Chapel Hill, NC: Center for Ecozoic Studies.

Bede Griffiths, 1989. *A New Vision of Reality.* Springfield, Illinois: Templegate Publishers.

Andrew Harvey, 2001. *The Way of Passion.* New York: Jeremy P Tarcher/Putnam.

John F. Haught, 2017. *The New Cosmic Story.* New Haven CT: Yale University Press.

Michael W. Higgins and Kevin Burns, 2012. *Genius Born of Anguish: The Life and legacy of Henri Nouwen.* Mahwah NJ: Paulist Press.

Karl Jaspers, 1953. *The Origin and Goal of Human History.* New Haven CT: Yale University Press.

Beverly Lanzetta, 1985. *Path of the Heart.* New York: Paragon House.

Erwin Laszlo, 1998. *The Whispering Pond: A Personal Guide to the Emerging Vision of Science.* Shaftsbury, Dorset UK: Element.

Ervin Laszlo, 2006. *Science and the Reenchantment of the Cosmos.* Rochester, Vermont: Inner Traditions.

Ervin Laszlo, 2017. *The Intelligence of the Cosmos.* Rochester, Vermont: Inner Traditions.

Sam Mackintosh, 2019. A Legacy for My Grandchildren. *Origins, The Bulletin of International Big History Association.* Vol X, No. 1.

Joanna Rogers Macy,1983. *Despair and Personal Power in the Nuclear Age.* Philadelphia, PA: New Society Publishers.

Thomas Merton, 1963. *Hagia Sophia* <btpen.wordpress.com/2013/04/26/hagia-sophia-by-thomas-merton/amp/>.

J. Philip Newell, 2008. *Christ of the Celts.* San Francisco, CA: Jossey-Bass.

F. David Peat, 1987. *Synchronicity: The Bridge Between Matter and Mind.* New York: Bantam Books.

John Polkinghorne, 1998. *Belief in God In an Age of Science.* New Haven: Yale University Press.

Carlo Rovelli, 2014. *Reality Is Not What It Seems.* New York: Riverhead Books.

Jan van Ruusbroec, 1986. *Spiritual Espousals, The Sparkling Stones, and Other Works (Classis of Western Spirituality).* Mahwah NJ: Paulist Press

Lothar Schafer, 1997. *In Search of Divine Reality.* Fayetteville, Arkansas, The University of Arkansas Press.

Anthony Stevens, 1993. *Two Million-Year-Old Self.* College Station: Texas A&M University Press.

Brian Swimme, 1984. *The Universe Is a Green Dragon,* Sante Fe, New Mexico: Bear & Company, Inc.

Bibliography

Brian Swimme, 1989. "Cosmos as Primary Revelation", *Teilhard Perspectives* 22 (2): 80.

Brian Swimme, 2019. *Hidden Heart of the Cosmos.* Maryknoll, NY: Orbis Books.

Brian Swimme and Thomas Berry, 1992. *The Universe Story.* New York, NY: HarperCollins Publishers.

Charles T. Tart, 2009. *The End of Materialism: How Evidence of the Paranormal Is Bringing Science and Spirit Together.* Oakland CA: New Harbinger Publications.

Richard Tarnas, 2006. *Cosmos and Psyche: Intimations of a New World.* New York NY: Plume Books.

Teresa of Avila, 1976. "The Way of Perfection" translated by Otilio Rodriguez O.C.D. and Kieran Kavanaugh, O.C.D., *The Collected Work of Teresa of Avila.* Washington, D.C.: ICS Publications.

Teresa of Avila, 1987. *Transformation of the Symbol of the Interior Castle. Teresianum* – Ephemerides Carmeliticae.

Mary Evelyn Tucker and John Grimm, eds, 2009. *The Christian Future and the Fate of the Earth.* Maryknoll, NY: Orbis Books.

Mary Evelyn Tucker, John Grimm, and Andrew Augyal, 2019. *Thomas Berry: A Biography.* New York NY: Columbia University Press.

Edward C Whitmont, 1993.*The Alchemy of Healing.* Berkeley, CA: North Atlantic Books.

Fred Alan Wolf, 1999. *The Spiritual Universe.* Portsmouth, NH: Moment Point Press.

Jerry R. Wright, 2018. *Reimaging God and Religion.* Asheville, North Carolina, Chiron Publications.

John Yungblut, 1979. *Discovering God Within.* Philadelphia, PA: Westminster Press.

John Yungblut, 1983. *Speaking as One Friend to Another on the Mystical Way Forward.* Wallingford, PA: Pendle Hill Pamphlet #249.

Mary Conrow Coelho has a background in both science and theology. She taught high school biology in the American Community School in Buenos Aires. She has an MDiv degree from Union Theological Seminary and a PhD from Fordham University. She is the author of *Awakening Universe, Emerging Personhood: The Power of Contemplation on an Evolving Universe*, several articles, and a Pendle Hill Pamphlet, *Recovering Sacred Presence in a Disenchanted World*. She has led a number of workshops and founded and led groups on spirituality, mysticism and the universe story. She has been a watercolor painter for many years, becoming a signature member of the Northeast Watercolor Society and the Catherine Lorillard Art Club in New York City.

CPSIA information can be obtained
at www.ICGtesting.com
Printed in the USA
LVHW072311050122
707923LV00022B/1455